'I must be a real damper to your ego, Chase, refusing to be bowled over by your good looks and lashings of charm.'

'Are you sure?' he asked huskily, fully aware of the panic rising in Melanie's eyes. 'Quite sure?'

'Sure about what?'

'Your immunity,' he prompted. 'You wouldn't be afraid of me, would you?' he asked, moving even closer. 'And, as you're not afraid, you won't object if I put you to the test, will you, Melanie?'

Dear Reader

There's something different about Mills & Boon romances! From now on, in the front pages of all our stories, you'll find a short extract to tempt you to read on, a biography about the author and a letter from the editor, all of which we hope will welcome you to our heart-warming world of romance. What's more, if you've got any comments or suggestions to make about Mills & Boon's stories, drop us a line; we'll be glad to hear from you.

See you next month!

The Editor

Margaret Callaghan was born in Liverpool in 1953. She was brought up and educated in the nearby market town of Ormskirk, Lancashire, famed for its gingerbread and its unusual parish church boasting both steeple and tower. Margaret is married with one daughter, Laura, and has lived close to beautiful Cannock Chase in Staffordshire for several years. She currently teaches English at a West Bromwich comprehensive school. Her loves include French wine, French food, French holidays, and, of course, in true romance tradition, husband, Rob.

Recent titles by the same author:

SUBSTITUTE HUSBAND

PASSING STRANGERS

BY

MARGARET CALLAGHAN

MILLS & BOON LIMITED
ETON HOUSE 18-24 PARADISE ROAD
RICHMOND SURREY TW9 1SR

First published in Great Britain 1992
by Mills & Boon Limited

© Margaret Callaghan 1992

Australian copyright 1992
Philippine copyright 1992
This edition 1992

ISBN 0 263 77545 3

Set in Times Roman 10 on 12 pt.
01-9205-54286 C

Made and printed in Great Britain

CHAPTER ONE

THE phone rang. Melanie Sandford paused for a moment, debating whether to let it ring, sorely tempted to ignore it. She had a deadline to meet as well as Ben to pick up in another half-hour. Once he was home from school all thought of work could be forgotten till his bedtime. And she'd promised this chapter by five o'clock. With another two thousand words still to type she'd be pushing it.

Stifling her annoyance, she crossed to the tiny hall and lifted the receiver. 'Yes?' she enquired, not bothering to give her number.

'Ah! The elusive lady herself. Miss Sandford, Miss Melanie Sandford?' purred a deep, husky voice.

'Speaking.'

'So, you really do exist, then? I was beginning to believe you were a figment of someone's imagination. Why don't you answer my letters, Miss Sandford? If I've written once in the past three months I must have written a dozen times and all to no avail. Such a waste of paper, don't you think, not to mention my time and effort?'

'Perhaps if I knew your name I might consider answering your question,' Melanie replied curtly, stiffening instinctively. She didn't need a name. There was only one person it could possibly be. The pile of letters lay in a drawer, unanswered but not unread, the steadily increased amount offered in each merely strengthening her resolve not to sell.

'Come, now, you're playing games with me. I can't believe you really don't know who I am.'

'Oh, I think I can hazard a guess,' Melanie informed him coolly. 'There's only one person whose ego could be matched by the size of his bank-balance. Well, save your breath, Mr Banister, as well as your time and effort—and don't forget the price of the postage stamps,' she forced in sweetly. 'I should hate you to throw good money after bad. I'm not selling. Not today, not to-morrow, not next week, or next year. Not ever. The cottage is mine, and it's not for sale.'

She replaced the receiver and leaned back against the wall, her insides churning. How ridiculous, letting some strange man have this effect on her. He was probably fifty and fat and balding, not young and handsome to match his sexy voice. She caught sight of her reflection in the mirror on the wall. Her cheeks were stained with pink, her eyes deep velvet pools filled with foreboding. She shook her head. The cottage was hers, hers and Ben's. No one could take it away from her. All the money in the world couldn't buy her. Besides, Hilary would have fought tooth and nail to keep the estate intact, and, now that she was gone, Melanie would do likewise.

The phone rang again, causing her to jump.

'Don't hang up,' he entreated urgently. 'Just give me five minutes; it won't be time wasted, I promise you.'

'Why?' Melanie asked warily.

'Why?' He laughed, a deep, throaty sound that was music to her ears. 'I'm a businessman, Miss Sandford. Time is money. And a few minutes spent explaining could be valuable to both of us.'

'I doubt it,' Melanie informed him.

'You haven't heard my latest offer,' he pointed out.

'I don't need to. It may be just a heap of bricks and mortar to you, but this is my home; I'm happy here and I don't want to leave. The sooner you believe it, the better it will be for both of us.'

'Everyone has their price, my dear,' he contradicted silkily. 'We just haven't reached yours yet. Why not name your amount? It could save us both a lot of bother.'

'You seem to have a hearing impediment,' Melanie observed with a touch of asperity. 'Perhaps I ought to raise my voice, spell it out in words of one syllable?'

'I'm a very persistent man, Miss Sandford. I'm not going to take no for an answer.'

'Sorry to disoblige you, Mr Banister, but you couldn't be more wrong. The only answer you're likely to have from me is thanks, but no, thanks. Now, if you don't mind, I've got work to do, and, as you *so* succinctly phrased it, time is money, for me at any rate. Good afternoon.'

The cheek of the man, she seethed, returning to her typewriter. The naked arrogance. How dared he assume she was holding out for a higher amount? Just because he had no principles, he blithely assumed everyone else was just as corrupt. And Hilary had been right, hadn't she, worrying about the future of the Lynacre estate once Chase Banister got his hands on it? Melanie had done her best to reassure her but it hadn't been easy, Hilary obviously knowing her nephew too well. The rumours had flown thick and fast since Hilary's death, but, whatever plan he'd set his mind on, Chase Banister wasn't going to find it easy to implement, not with Melanie to contend with. As far as she was concerned he was wasting his time. She'd never sell. And he'd get the message. The penny would drop—eventually.

The phone rang as she was feeding another sheet of paper into the rollers, and Melanie's impatience turned to annoyance. 'The answer's still no,' she rasped into the receiver.

'Melanie?' queried a different voice. 'Is something wrong?'

The tension drained away. 'Sorry, Suzanne,' Melanie apologised with a chuckle. 'I thought it was someone else.'

'I'm glad I'm not in his shoes, then, always assuming it *was* a man raising your hackles. Anyone I know?'

'I doubt it. Just someone with an exaggerated idea of his own importance and a warped idea of the power of money.'

'He *has* upset you, hasn't he?' Suzanne chuckled in turn. 'Now this I've simply got to hear—but later. It's nearly three-fifteen and the kids will be coming out of school. I promised Jonathan I'd take him to the park if the afternoon was fine, and I wondered if Ben would like to come too. I've packed a picnic, so we'll be a couple of hours if that's all right with you.'

'Bless you, Suzanne, you're a life-saver. I'm up to my eyebrows in typing and I simply must get this lot finished today. What time shall I pick him up?'

'Does seven o'clock suit?' her friend asked.

'Seven o'clock's perfect. See you then.'

Melanie turned back to her work, but she'd lost her concentration, her mind wandering along pathways of its own, and the next few pages were so riddled with mistakes that she gave up. Crumpling yet another spoiled sheet into a ball, she flung it in the general direction of the waste bin and, stifling a sigh, stood up and stretched her limbs. She'd take a break, a ten-minute ramble round the garden before tackling anew the last few pages.

She collected a drink along the way, a tall glass of well-chilled orange juice, and then ambled down to her favourite corner. Most of the garden was functional, the rows and rows of neat vegetables vigorous testimony to her hard work throughout the winter, but she'd kept a corner for herself and Ben, a small square laid with paving stones where Ben had ridden his bike when he was small, surrounded on three sides by narrow borders packed with summer bedding plants she'd grown herself. A honeysuckle twined along a terrace, hiding an ugly stone wall, and the weathered wooden bench looked as if it had always been there. Melanie curled up on this now, sipping her drink, leaning back, relaxing in her pocket of peace.

If she closed her eyes she could be a million miles from anywhere, just the steady drone of the bees and the distant bark of a dog breaking the silence. The sun and the heat were soporific and Melanie's eyelids began to droop. She'd have to make a move in a moment or she'd never drag herself back to her work, but still she sat on, thoughts drifting.

So much had changed in a few short months that she wasn't yet sure of her bearings. She was alone again, apart from Ben, and in the confusion and pain following Hilary's death hadn't quite managed to pull herself together. But still, she had her security and that was the important thing. The cottage belonged to her now, was her lifeline. Everything else would fall into place in time.

It was dark in the cottage after the dazzling sunshine but her eyes quickly adjusted, and she was humming lightly as she resumed her work, Chapter Six of *A Song of Love*, a historical romance by Ormskirk's resident author, and the neat pile of papers mounted steadily as Melanie's fingers flew across the keys.

It was a stop-gap occupation but another piece of luck, keeping her busy as well as providing a welcome source of income, and, besides, was excellent practice for rusty skills. And, once she'd built up her confidence, she'd see about applying for a more permanent office position in the nearby town.

By five o'clock she'd proof-read and corrected her day's work. She's just have time to drop it off and catch the shops before closing time. As she rummaged for the car keys in the kitchen drawer her eye was caught by the pile of letters, each one dominated by the bold, sprawling signature. Chase Banister. A very persistent man. Chase Banister, a thorn in Melanie's side. She heard again his voice over the phone, deep, velvet, vibrant with an edge of impatience, and conjured up an imaginary picture of him. A shiver ran down her spine. She hadn't heard the last of him, she was sure of that, and, illogically, she was glad.

'Hi.'

Melanie straightened her back and gazed up at the figure leaning casually against the jamb of the open gate. It was hot in the garden, the hottest day of the year so far, but she wanted to get things tidied up before the weekend arrived and Ben took over.

'You'll fry in this heat. Didn't anyone ever tell you about the power of the midday sun?' the man continued, moving away from the gate and picking his way across the path of broken paving stones that bisected the vegetable plot.

'Didn't anyone ever tell *you* that it was wrong to trespass on other people's property?' Melanie retorted, something vaguely familiar about his voice troubling her. She found herself wondering too just where he'd appeared from. She hadn't heard a car and, living where she did, wasn't used to people 'simply passing by'.

'Trespass is one of those funny laws,' he informed her. 'You can only prosecute if you can prove damage or malicious intent. My presence here is entirely honest and innocent, I assure you.'

'But I've only your word for that. Something I do remember being told over and over again from the age of two upwards was never to speak to strange men,' she countered coldly as he drew near.

'That one's easily rectified,' he replied, reaching the end of her row and halting. 'I'll introduce myself. Once we know each other, well, we can't possibly be strangers, can we?'

As he finished speaking Melanie stepped back, instinctively keeping her distance, a powerful surge of emotion catching her off guard. As he'd drawn nearer she'd turned sideways to meet him full on and was no longer dazzled by the glare of the sun. She stared up at him, stunned. His brown eyes were crinkled at the corners, the easy smile inviting, disarming. It was a face she had never seen before and yet a face she recognised immediately.

'Let me guess,' he said, holding out a hand. 'Miss Melanie Sandford? You're exactly as I imagined you to be. And I'm——'

'Chase Banister,' she interrupted drily, her racing mind having sifted all the clues and put the voice into context. 'I should have known.'

There was an awkward pause. Melanie leaned on the hoe, conscious of the sight she must present, old patched jeans grimy at the knees where she'd been kneeling in the soil, the faded blouse damp with perspiration. A lock of hair had escaped from its pony-tail and she pushed it back behind an ear, trailing a smudge of dirt across her cheek. Her hands were hot and sticky, a stark contrast to his, which were cool; long, tapering fingers gripping hers for a moment.

She had to crane her neck to meet his gaze, a gaze surprisingly frank and open, which swept over her, missing not a single detail, she was sure: the trim figure underneath the well-worn clothes, the beads of sweat on her forehead, the pulse racing away at the base of her throat. She flushed underneath his scrutiny but he smiled, sensing her unease, and her heart turned over.

'Why have you come?' she asked, when the silence had stretched out between them.

'You're a difficult lady to pin down,' he explained. 'You refuse to answer my letters, hang up when I phone. The next step was obvious.'

'Not to me,' she replied with more than a degree of hostility. 'You could have saved yourself a journey. Surely you're not so thick-skinned that you can't take a gentle hint?'

'Hardly gentle,' he murmured, mouth twitching slightly. 'I'd hate to really cross you, really incur your wrath, if this is your idea of the soft brush-off.'

'I'm not used to people who blithely ignore my wishes,' Melanie told him coldly.

'And I'm not used to beautiful young women of such fierce determination,' he countered lightly.

'Is that a compliment?' she asked, stiffening.

'It could be. Why?'

'Flattery won't work either, Mr Banister. You're wasting your time.'

'Call me Chase,' he insisted. 'Mr Banister's much too formal. Besides, I feel I know you already from Aunt Hilary's letters. You were good to her; I'm grateful.'

Melanie flushed. 'I merely did the job I was paid to do. If anything, Hilary was good to me. You never came to visit,' she added curtly. 'Why?'

He threw back his head and laughed, a rich, deep sound she recognised from the telephone conversation two days before.

'You don't mince words, do you?' he asked, though not unkindly.

'I'm not into diplomacy, wrapping something up in a dozen words when three or four will do. Hilary was lonely. Oh, yes, she had me and a whole host of friends who made sure she never lacked for company, but she needed her family, not a stranger keeping house, cooking, ironing, shopping, reading her the news. She deserved better than that.'

A single eyebrow rose. 'She deserved better than me, you mean.'

'You *were* conspicuous by your absence,' she needled.

'Perhaps I had a reason.'

'I'm sure you did.'

Impasse. Another awkward pause. Melanie stood, biting her lower lip, waiting for him to leave. He wasn't welcome here. He was too late, six years too late. Hilary Reynolds had been dead just three months and here he was, the ubiquitous vulture hell-bent on picking over the bones.

She glanced up. He was watching her and she flushed again under the close scrutiny, instinctively straightening her spine, lifting her chin.

'You don't like me, do you?' he asked.

'How can I possibly dislike someone I met only ten minutes ago?' Melanie countered.

'But you do,' he insisted. 'You've made up your mind. You're not interested in my explanations. I never came to visit when she was alive; I'm up here like a shot now that she's dead. It isn't difficult to follow the workings of your mind.'

'How astute you are,' Melanie snapped. 'Well, for once, you're right—you seem to have the message. Progress indeed. Now all that's needed is for you to accept my assurance that the cottage is not for sale and you can crawl back to your fancy London office with your fancy London ways and leave us all in peace.'

'Oo-oh! The lady has thorns. And I thought Northerners were noted for their hospitality,' he mocked, not a bit put out.

'We are,' she agreed. 'But generally we like to issue our own invitations and then we tend to opt for people we like.'

'You might like me, given time.'

'I doubt it.'

'Why not try me? We could both be pleasantly surprised.'

'You don't give up, do you?' she asked. 'You're like a dog with a bone.'

'Is that a compliment?' he teased, brown eyes crinkling.

'I'm sure you'll take it as one, turn persistence into a virtue.'

'And isn't it?'

'Not always. In some cases it's just another word for stubbornness, arrogance, an inflated ego.'

'And which of those applies to me?' he asked. 'I'm sure you *have* made up your mind.'

'Take your pick,' she retorted sweetly, raising another laugh.

'First impressions can be very misleading,' he warned.

'You forget, Mr Banister, I've had three months to make up my mind.'

'Chase, please,' he insisted. 'Why stand on ceremony when we've known each other such a long time? So, your mind's made up, is it? Nothing I can say or do will alter your opinion?'

'Not a thing,' she replied with a satisfied smile.

'And isn't that a form of arrogance, too?' he queried.

'I beg your pardon?' Melanie bristled.

'People change, circumstances change. People who cling to rigid ideas in the face of progress tend to get left behind, caught up in a time-warp. You have to move with the times, and that includes revising your opinions. You're entitled to your views, Miss Sandford—Melanie,' he corrected with a bitter twist of his lips. 'But clinging to them in the face of fresh evidence is plain intractability.'

'Have you finished?' Melanie demanded, eyes flashing dangerously.

'What's the matter, can't you take the truth? Haven't you heard the proverb about living in glass houses?'

'Oh, I can take the truth, all right, but I don't have to listen to your twisted version of it.'

'It's merely my opinion, but feel free to contradict. Who knows? You might even change my mind.'

'I might, if it was important enough.'

Chase merely shrugged, thrust his hands into trouser pockets, and gazed out over the hedge at the big house in the distance.

Melanie followed the line of his gaze. Hilary Reynolds's house; his house now, she supposed. She swallowed her irritation, her innate sense of fairness rising to the surface. Until recently Chase had been her employer's nephew, absentee, but related nonetheless. Had he arrived any time during the past six years his welcome would have been completely different. And, in that case, didn't she owe it to Hilary to make an effort now?

'You'll want to have a look round before you go back,' she murmured. 'How about a cold drink while I root out the key?'

He turned and smiled, and once again, absurdly, she felt a strange tug at her heart. 'An olive branch?' he queried. 'Thank you. That would be nice. I'll sit out here if that's all right with you. It's much too hot to be indoors.'

Melanie inclined her head and watched as he sauntered over to the bench in the corner. She turned and went inside, washing her hands and face and tugging a hasty comb through her long blonde hair in an effort to make herself more presentable. Quite why she needed to bother she didn't stop to analyse, but it would have had little to do with the stranger now making himself at home in her garden, she was sure of that much. Five minutes later she rejoined him, carrying a tray which she set down on a tree-stump.

'Iced tea. I hope you like it. If not, there's always orange juice.'

'Iced tea will be fine,' he insisted. 'I haven't had it in years and yet it's perfect for a day like this. I wonder why it hasn't caught on?'

'It probably has in warmer climes,' Melanie observed. 'We're not exactly known for our long, hot summers.'

'No, I suppose not.'

They slipped into silence, sipping the refreshing drink, Melanie acutely aware of the man at her side. She felt uneasy in his presence, but couldn't work out why.

He was stunningly good-looking but it was more than that. He leaned back on the bench, closing his eyes against the glare of the sun, and she studied him surreptitiously lest he glance up, catching her off guard. Thirty, thirty-two, she guessed, long and lean, the sun-bronzed angles of his face seeming cruel till he smiled, transforming his features. Dark hair, well cut with a hint of a wave, one rebellious lock falling over his forehead. He was impeccably dressed in deceptively casual fashion; beige open-necked shirt and brown canvas trousers that, even Melanie could see, hadn't been bought in any of the chain stores. And he oozed masculinity, a primitive sexuality that caused unexpected stirrings deep inside her body.

He opened his eyes suddenly and she glanced away, the blush rising in her cheeks, but he appeared not to notice. He drained his glass and she refilled it from the jug, adding the slices of lemon. Their fingers touched briefly as he took the glass from her and Melanie suppressed a cry as the waves of electricity travelled the length of her body, shocking her.

'Is it always so quiet here?' he asked, seemingly unaware of the static crackling on the air between them.

'Mostly,' Melanie answered, controlling her emotions with a huge effort of concentration. 'We're part of the town and yet not part of the town, if you follow my meaning. The best of both worlds, I suppose,' she rushed on. 'On one side there are miles and miles of fields, hedgerows, the occasional farmhouse and outbuildings. Yet, if I turn around, I'm just a stone's throw from all the amenities of a thriving market town. It's not a bad place to live.'

'Hm. I'm amazed it's so flat. I've heard of the Lancashire plain, but this reminds me of Norfolk without the Broads.'

Melanie smiled at the analogy. She waved an arm, taking in the miles and miles of farmland. 'These were the mosses,' she explained. 'Water-logged areas fit for nothing till they were drained, resulting in some of the richest soils in the country.'

'Which you've utilised fully, I notice,' he observed, rising, stretching his legs. 'What on earth do you do with all these vegetables?'

'Some of them I use, some of them I freeze, the surplus I sell.'

'Here? From the cottage?'

'No, silly. At the market. I have a couple of regular contacts who are always glad to take my produce.'

'You can't possibly make a living out of that, can you?' he enquired, eyebrows rising.

'No, but it helps.'

'So just what do you do, aside from looking after my Aunt Hilary?'

Melanie shrugged. 'That's it. I'm a housekeeper, or I was until recently. Now...' She shrugged again, loath to give anything away to this man who seemed intent on tearing her still fragile world to pieces. She found herself prevaricating, instinctively protecting herself. 'I'm between jobs, as they say, but I manage.'

'Isn't that rather a strange occupation for a young woman, keeping house, I mean? Didn't you want a career, one of the more conventional jobs? There must be plenty of opportunities in a town this size, or in Liverpool or Manchester, Preston even.'

'I had my reasons,' she evaded, unconsciously echoing an earlier comment.

'I'm sure you did,' he parried, voice gently mocking.

Melanie's colour rose but she bit her lip, swallowing an angry retort.

'I'm sorry, I was prying. That was rude of me. You've every right to tell me to mind my own business.'

She glanced up. He appeared perfectly serious, velvet eyes watching her, a tiny frown creasing his brow. 'It doesn't matter,' she replied evenly. 'It's a question I've been asked before and I don't suppose you'll be the last to raise it.'

'It doesn't excuse my impertinence. I'm not usually so uncouth, I promise you.'

'Forget it.' Melanie picked up the glasses, putting them on the tray, closing the subject.

Chase continued to watch her for a moment and then he shrugged. 'If you'll let me have that key I'll be off, then. Unless you'd like to show me round? I'd be glad of your company,' he added, sensing her surprise. 'And you know the house. It would be a help, if you can spare the time.'

Melanie opened her mouth to speak, fully intending to say no, when unexpectedly she nodded. 'All right,' she agreed solemnly. 'Give me five minutes to change and I'll be with you.'

They strolled down the lane. It was much too hot to rush, in any case. 'We could take my car,' Melanie suggested. 'It isn't very far but if you're out of practice——'

'I can manage, thanks,' Chase interrupted smoothly. 'And now who's being controversial? I thought we'd called a truce.'

'Whatever gave you that idea?' Melanie asked, flashing him a smile.

'Just an impression,' he replied, but he was smiling too, and the five minutes or so it took to cover the rest of the distance were spent in easy conversation.

A car was parked outside the gates, a metallic-blue BMW.

'Mine,' he told her in answer to her startled look. 'I wanted to get the feel of the place, peer in through the windows, absorb the atmosphere. Then I spotted your cottage at the end of the lane and decided to wander over.'

'Why not drive over?' Melanie asked, absurdly annoyed and not sure why. After all, he did own the estate now and, if he chose to sneak in the back way, well, that was his prerogative.

Chase raised an eyebrow. 'If I'd rolled up in that you'd have known straight away who I was. You were hostile enough to start with,' he explained. 'If I'd given you thirty seconds' warning you'd have disappeared flat. I needed to talk to you, had to reach you somehow. I took a chance you'd be in and it paid off.'

'You're so clever, aren't you?' Melanie snapped, angry with him but a lot more furious with herself for allowing him to creep under her defences, worm his way so easily into her confidence. She'd come across men like him before, men who wheedled what they wanted out of susceptible females old enough to know better, men who flattered, cajoled, turned on the charm like water gushing from a tap.

She halted, facing him, colour flooding her cheeks, her temper held in check with difficulty. 'You think you've out-manoeuvred me, caught me on the hop, but you haven't,' she informed him icily. 'I guessed who you were. As soon as you opened your mouth I knew. And you're still wasting your time. Half an hour's pleasant conversation over a glass of iced tea isn't likely to sway me. I was being polite, extending common courtesy. How ill-mannered of you to abuse my hospitality.'

'There is another way of looking at it,' he pointed out mildly.

'Oh, there's always another side to everything,' Melanie retorted, tossing her hair over her shoulders and storming ahead, the lines of her body quivering in suppressed fury as she lengthened her stride. 'You'll twist it all your way, I'm sure. You're very good with words, too good by half. But you're banging your head against a brick wall. The cottage can't be bought. No amount of money could induce me to sell. Not to you, not to anyone.'

'Why won't you sell? Why? Give me one good reason,' he demanded as they reached the gates.

She spun round, bristling. 'Do you have a house, Mr Banister? A home? Somewhere that *you* belong?'

'Chase, for heaven's sake. Let's not go back to all that "yes, Miss Sandford, no, Mr Banister" nonsense. And no, Melanie, I don't have a home. I've moved about so much in the past few years that I've practically lived out of a suitcase. I'm back in England now, for good. I'll find somewhere permanent eventually.'

'Why?' she asked.

'Why what?'

'Why will you find somewhere permanent? What's wrong with travelling round, moving around, living out of a suitcase?'

'Nothing, if that's how you want it to be. But I want to settle down, put down roots——'

'Ha!' she interrupted, her voice rising despite her efforts to remain in control. 'He wants to put down roots but he cares nothing about tearing up mine. I live here, I'm happy here, I belong here. Why can't you leave me in peace?'

'It's a good offer, Melanie. You wouldn't be losing out. You could keep your roots, choose your house, choose your own site even. You could live anywhere you wanted.'

'I want,' she insisted coldly, 'to live here.'

'And what happens to this house in the meanwhile?' he asked.

'I don't know what you mean,' she replied stonily.

'Look at it, Melanie. It's falling to bits. Even you must be able to see that. It wants pulling down, redeveloping. It would cost a fortune to renovate and then who'd want to live there? Who could afford to live there? The house is a white elephant.'

'You're simply making excuses,' she retorted, turning away, leaning her arms on the top of the gate.

'I'm being rational, level-headed——'

'Pig-headed more likely,' she muttered, half under her breath.

'I haven't a monopoly on obstinacy,' he rasped. 'Listen to me, you little fool.' He grabbed her shoulders, spinning her round to face him, and Melanie squirmed under his touch, but the fingers bit more cruelly into her flesh, pinning her against the wrought iron.

His eyes held hers, deep velvet pools, fringed by the longest lashes Melanie had ever seen. She raised her chin defiantly, challenging him, her own eyes diamond-hard, returning his gaze unflinchingly.

'I'm listening,' she goaded. 'I haven't much choice, have I, Chase? I'm a captive audience and, believe me,

I'm all ears. I'll listen. I'll listen to every single word you say, and do you know something? When you've finished I'll give you my answer. Perhaps then you'll pay me the courtesy of listening to me.'

Abruptly he released her, and Melanie's knees gave way. She clutched at the gate, but it was Chase's arms which shot out to steady her, the fingers no longer digging in, simply holding, supporting, strangely comforting, yet inexplicably disconcerting. For a fraction of a second everything tilted, swam before her eyes, and then his face moved into focus, the harsh lines dissolving as he leaned closer, concern clouding his features, concern giving way to another expression, fleeting, imaginary, inflammatory, and Melanie held her breath, expecting him to kiss her, wanting him to kiss her.

Chase stepped back, releasing her again, severing the eye contact, and a wave of disappointment swamped her.

'I'll see myself round,' he said curtly, dismissively, already moving away. 'I've taken up enough of your time today.'

'If that's what you want,' Melanie murmured, rubbing her arms where his fingers had left an impression.

He shot her a strange, piercing glance. 'It isn't, not especially. But it's probably better this way.'

'Yes. I suppose so.' Melanie's voice was bleak. 'I'll say goodbye, then.'

'Goodbye? No, Melanie.' He smiled, but the light didn't reach his eyes. 'I've messed it up today but I haven't given up. I'll never give up, not until I get what I want. And Melanie,' he added matter-of-factly, the complete lack of emotion in his words underlining their chilling ring of truth, 'I always get what I want—in the end. I'll be seeing you.'

He vaulted the gate and strode purposefully up the drive, never once glancing back to where Melanie continued to stand, watching him out of sight, her emotions in turmoil.

She shivered, and then smiled a grim smile. Forewarned was forearmed. She'd be waiting.

CHAPTER TWO

THE phone rang. Melanie stood and watched it, mesmerised, unconsciously counting the rings in her head. When it got to ten she reached out a tentative hand. 'Yes?' she enquired, and then held her breath.

'Good morning, Melanie,' drawled the by now familiar voice in her ear, triggering a ripple of excitement.

'Good morning to you,' she replied, her own voice not quite steady.

'You're still talking to me, then? I did wonder, especially when you took so long to answer.'

'I was out in the garden,' she lied. 'I didn't hear it at first.'

'Busy?' he asked.

'Just weeding,' she replied, crossing her fingers at the second untruth.

'Is it important?'

'Important enough. Why?' she asked, her heart beginning to go thump, thump, thump in her breast.

'If it's not too important I thought you might like to have lunch with me. A sort of peace-offering for yesterday's ill-humour.'

'There's no need,' she told him. 'Yesterday's over and forgotten.'

'Good. I'm glad you're so forgiving. Have lunch with me anyway.'

'Why?'

A low chuckle rippled down the phone line, causing her to smile.

'You've a very suspicious mind, young lady,' he chided. 'Does there have to be a reason? No, don't bother to answer that one. I've a dozen reasons. It's Thursday, the sun's shining, the birds are singing, I'm hungry—or I will be in another hour—and I'd like very much to take a young, rather beautiful, rather fiery lady out for a meal.'

'You're seven short,' she informed him, colouring at his words, glad he couldn't see the blush creeping into her cheeks.

'And you're splitting hairs. Pick you up in an hour?'

'I haven't said yes yet,' she retorted, knowing full well she had no intentions of doing otherwise.

'Melanie?'

'Yes, Chase?'

'There, you've said it! See you soon.'

Melanie was left holding the receiver, her face a mixture of emotions, shadow and light alternating in her eyes. She wasn't sure it was a good idea. He was an attractive man, just the sort of man she had avoided like the plague. The Chase Banisters of this world didn't waste time on women, they used them. And, when they'd taken what they wanted, they tossed them aside, instantly forgotten, instantly replaced. Men like Chase were trouble, trouble with a capital T. And wasn't Ben a constant reminder of just how much trouble?

Even so, she hummed as she went upstairs to change, dipping her head as she passed under the low doorway of her bedroom. It was a tiny cottage, obviously built as a farm-worker's house, and too small at times for an active child, but Melanie loved it and couldn't imagine living anywhere else now.

The cottage hadn't exactly gone with the job, Hilary Reynolds having advertised for a live-in housekeeper, but as soon as Melanie had set eyes on it she'd known that it was just what she wanted. She'd passed the empty cottage every day, of course, but one morning she'd had time to spare, had taken Ben for a longer walk than usual and on impulse she'd pushed open the heavy front door. It was like a dolls' house, tiny rooms, low ceilings, doorways you regularly cracked your head on, and yet she loved it.

It had been neglected but that didn't stop her. Hilary wasn't too sure, pointing out the drawbacks, the numerous imperfections, but Melanie had talked her round, her enthusiasm infectious. 'Give it a three-month trial,' she had urged. 'If it doesn't work, or you're not happy, I'll move back in with you and that will be the end of the matter.'

But it had worked. They'd both been happy. Melanie had bought a car, an old Mini, and could be up at the big house almost before the phone stopped ringing. The arrangement had been ideal, Hilary maintaining her independence and yet with Melanie close at hand if needed, Melanie herself taking pride in the first real home she'd had, hers and Ben's.

When Hilary died Melanie had expected to find herself homeless, but the old lady had had a surprise in store. The Lynacre estate was left to Chase Banister, Hilary's only surviving relative, but the cottage with its garden and a thirty-metre border of land around it was Melanie's.

She halted in front of her wardrobe, stiffening instinctively as she remembered the motive behind the casual invitation to lunch. The cottage was hers, she reassured herself, hers to keep, and keep it she would. Chase Banister might have other ideas, but that was his problem and she wasn't about to let it spoil her day.

He was bang on time, his appreciative glance sweeping over her as Melanie opened the door to his ring.

'Ready?' he asked as she stepped out to join him. 'Good lord, a very rare specimen indeed. Don't you know it's obligatory to keep a man waiting? Ten minutes at the very least,' he teased.

'That's a very sexist comment,' Melanie rebuked him. 'Anyway, I'm no ordinary woman, as you'll find out in time.'

'Is that a warning or a promise?' he asked, helping her into the car and slipping into the driver's seat beside her.

'Wait and see,' she retorted, a hint of a smile on her face. 'Wait and see.'

She had expected he'd take her to Southport, but to Melanie's surprise Chase set off down the lanes, the powerful engine purring like a sleek cat as they brushed the outskirts of the town and headed east.

'You seem to know your way around,' she observed, impressed.

'Not really. I have it on good authority that it's market day in Ormskirk and was told to avoid the town centre at all cost. At the moment I'm following my nose. When I get us lost I'm relying on you to bail us out. We've plenty of time, though. I've booked a table for one-thirty. A place called the Haywain. Ever been?'

Melanie nodded. She had, but not for a while, she told him, further impressed at the choice of venue. By accident or design Chase had managed to pick what was undoubtedly the best restaurant in the area.

She hadn't known what to wear, but was glad now she'd made an effort. The devil inside her had nearly gained the upper hand. She'd almost come casual, too casual, itching to see the expression on his face when she turned up in trousers and a T-shirt, but her other half, the sensible half, had intervened and she'd opted for a summer dress, a deceptively simple outfit in dusky pink silk, sleeveless with a tiny mandarin collar, the button-through bodice emphasising her high, taut breasts, the skirt gliding over her hips and ending a demure inch and a half above the knee. She'd had it some time but the quality was undeniable, the style almost classic, and the colour simply perfect for her pale golden hair.

Chase wore a suit, dark grey with the merest hint of a pin-stripe, and Melanie couldn't help the little thrill of pleasure that ran through her at being seen out with quite the best looking man she'd encountered for a long time. They weren't even friends, probably never would be, but that wasn't known to anyone watching. She caught the speculation in other women's eyes and was unexpectedly flattered.

They studied the menu over pre-lunch drinks.

'I'm starving,' Melanie confessed. 'And, looking at this, I'm really spoiled for choice.'

'What do you normally do for lunch?' he asked, turning his attention to the wine list.

'Oh, a sandwich, an apple, not a lot usually. I'm generally too busy to even notice what the time is.'

'But today you're starving?'

'Today I'm ravenous. Don't worry,' she told him. 'I'm not going to sit and pick at a lettuce leaf and half a tomato and call that a meal. Today I shall indulge myself, thanks to you.'

'My pleasure, *madame*.' He inclined his head. 'Though I must confess, there is an ulterior motive.'

'Oh, I'm sure there is,' she countered with a knowing smile. 'But business and pleasure don't mix, so I'm told.

You're a clever man, Chase, too clever to risk alienating me over lunch. You'll bide your time, wine me and dine me, and when you've judged the moment's right, when I'm softened up, had a drink or two, am feeling pleasantly replete, you'll pounce. It's insidious, ingenious, and a complete waste of time.'

The resonant laugh rang out, echoing round the room, drawing other glances, other smiles. 'It looks as though I've been rumbled,' he murmured. He picked up his glass. 'To Melanie Sandford,' he toasted. 'A very clever lady.'

'Thank you, sir,' she acknowledged lightly. 'I'll need to be if I'm dealing with you.'

'And to think, this time yesterday you didn't even like me.'

'Fishing for compliments, Chase? Sorry to disappoint you, but, as far as I'm concerned, nothing's changed, nothing's changed at all,' Melanie told him sweetly.

'A declaration of war?' he asked, voice hardening almost imperceptibly.

'Just a reminder that the peace treaty is simply that: an interruption of hostilities. And if you cast your mind back I think you'll find that you're the one who decided I didn't like you. I was much more open-minded.'

'That's not how I saw it.'

'No, but then you're so used to getting your own way that I'm sure you have difficulty seeing more than one side of anything.'

'Now who's making sweeping generalisations?' he demanded. 'Good grief, woman, you hardly know me.'

'Exactly,' she declared. 'I have my preconceived ideas, of course, but now that I've met you the picture's building up into something much more substantial.'

'You don't say,' he drawled, only the hard set of his lips betraying his annoyance. 'And how do I measure up so far? Don't be coy, Melanie. You can tell me. I can take it.'

'I wouldn't be too sure,' she goaded, the atmosphere shifting alarmingly. 'The male ego's surprisingly fragile when it's attacked by the fairer sex.'

'At least you didn't call yourself the gentler sex, the weaker sex. That's a misnomer if ever I heard one.'

'Women have their own defences; they need them. It's still a man's world, whatever's said about equality.'

'I hadn't taken you for a feminist,' he jeered.

'I'm not. That's another mistaken belief. Just because I refuse to lie down and be trampled all over I'm given a label, categorised, ridiculed, insulted.'

'You're twisting my words. It wasn't meant as an insult.'

'Come off it, Chase. Be honest. You knew what you were saying. Don't insult me even more by denying it.'

'Touchy, aren't you?' he needled. 'I wonder why? There's usually some deep-seated reason. Had a bad experience, Melanie? Did some man make a pass at you, insult your sensibilities?'

'Mind your own business,' she snapped, eyes flashing dangerously.

'Hit a nerve, did I?' he queried, a single eyebrow raised in mocking enquiry. 'Don't bother to deny it,' he drawled. 'It's as plain as the nose on your face. You should take it as a compliment, my dear. With your hackles raised and your stormy eyes you really are most attractive. Add to that a figure most women would give their eye-teeth to possess and you've a pretty explosive combination. I wouldn't be at all surprised if every full-

blooded male in the area wasn't beating a path to your
front door.'

'Have you quite finished your analysis?' she hissed,
controlling her anger with difficulty. He'd hit a nerve all
right, if he but knew it, and, although enough time had
passed to take away the sting of Jack's defection, it still
hurt that she'd been taken in, had trusted Jack, had given
him her love, had been let down so badly.

'It will do as a first consultation,' Chase replied easily.

'Any suggestions?' she enquired. 'Any treatment? Do
tell, Chase. It's a rare privilege having such an expert in
our midst. Another hour of this and I'll have buried all
my hang-ups for good. Mind you,' she added sweetly,
too sweetly, 'I'll have buried something else as well—
my axe, right between your ears.'

'Violence never solves anything,' he chided, but the
hard look had left his eyes and a smile was beginning
to play about the corners of his mouth. 'Why are we
fighting?' he asked, spreading his hands expansively.
'Can't we just be friends, or try to be, just for an hour
or so?'

Melanie swallowed a sigh, her anger dying. Around
them other couples sat and talked, sat hand in hand,
heads close, poring over a menu. Her gaze swept over
them. They all looked so happy, so content, so secure.
She blinked back a tear, bringing her gaze back to the
man sitting opposite. Was it such a tall order after all,
good food, good wine—she wasn't too sure about the
company—but she could try, couldn't she, just this once?
It wasn't exactly an olive branch he was offering but it
was probably the next best thing coming from a man
like Chase. His motives might be suspect but he'd made
an effort to defuse the situation, to salvage their meal,
and he needn't have bothered, given Melanie's over-

reaction. Wasn't it the least she could do, attempting to meet him halfway?

Chase had been watching her carefully and now he leaned forward, reaching for his drink, his eyes fastened on hers, questioningly. 'Pax?' he asked simply, raising his glass.

Melanie forced a smile. 'Pax,' she agreed.

It was a lovely meal and Melanie was glad that they'd called a truce. Chase *was* superb company, his easy manner disarming, relaxing, and she forgot for the moment the real reason he was there. Conversation seemed to flow, with none of those awkward pauses that seemed to beset people who didn't know each other very well, and, given the shaky start to the afternoon, their subsequent rapport seemed all the more amazing. He's turning on the charm, she tried to remind herself as the meal drew to a close, he's making a special effort. It's all part of a day's work to a man like Chase.

They were dazzled by the sun when they emerged into the fresh air, the first real spell of fine weather this year. It boded well for the summer, Melanie reflected, thinking of Ben and the long school holidays.

The restaurant was close to the canal and by tacit consent they turned away from the car park, strolling along the tow-path, peering occasionally into the weed-choked water for signs of fish and other aquatic wild life.

They came to a bridge and scrambled up the bank, Chase holding out a hand for Melanie, somewhat handicapped in her high heels. She hesitated a moment and then accepted his assistance, the touch of his fingers on hers sending waves of electricity running through her. She kept her eyes away from his, was annoyed at her reactions, hated the tell-tale rush of blood to her cheeks.

He was just another man, better looking than most, more
attractive than most, undeniably more dangerous than
most, but that was all. He meant nothing to her, nothing
at all, while Melanie had something that he wanted, and
wanted badly enough to give up a few hours of his time
to wine her and dine her, flatter her. She wasn't kidding
herself. She had her share of good looks but she wasn't
in his league at all. And once she'd signed on the dotted
line she wouldn't even be a distant memory. She smiled
grimly to herself. She had a surprise in store for Chase.
She wasn't about to be so obliging.

'You look like you've just lost a pound and found a
penny,' he observed, body close to hers as they leaned
on the parapet. 'Or is it indigestion from the gâteau?'

'Is that a hint that I ate too much?' Melanie countered, easing herself on to the low wall and swinging her
legs over so that they dangled above the water.

'Not really. Just a round-about way of asking why
you're scowling. It's a beautiful day, we've just had a
first-class meal, the company can't be faulted. I wondered what was wrong.'

'Modest, aren't we?' she chided. 'If you must know,
I was wondering when you would start your spiel—you
know, the sales patter. Isn't that next on the agenda?'
she asked matter-of-factly.

Chase removed his jacket, loosened his tie, his expression tightening slightly. He slung the jacket care-
lessly over the top of the wall and hitched himself up
beside her, so that they were seated side by side, Melanie
facing one way, Chase another, like sweethearts on a love
seat, Melanie thought, faintly amused.

'You don't have a very high opinion of me, do you?'
he asked.

'Do you care,' she countered, 'whether I like you or
hate you, respect you or otherwise? What am I supposed to say? I hardly know you. This time yesterday
we'd barely met. Twelve weeks' one-sided correspon-
dence doesn't give the clearest of pictures. I haven't a
lot to go on really. Just gut feelings, I suppose.' And
Hilary's comments on the rare occasion Chase had been
mentioned. Hilary had been fond of him of course, there
had never been any doubt about that. It was his business
dealings Hilary hadn't approved of. And, now that
Hilary was gone, here he was, Chase Banister, property
developer, about to extend his empire.

Uncannily he seemed to read her mind. 'You're still
convinced I treated Hilary badly. Isn't that the real reason
for your hostility? Would you be so quick to condemn
me if I'd danced attendance on her, pandered to her every
whim, crawled my way into her affections?'

'You didn't need to, did you?' she asked, careful to
keep the note of scorn from her voice. She didn't want
another row, now especially. Besides, it was much too
hot to quarrel.

'Hilary understood,' Chase replied. 'If I'd been in
England I'd have visited, but you don't have to believe
me. Continue to think the worst. It's of no consequence,
no consequence at all.'

'I didn't think it would be,' Melanie retorted, and then,
curiosity getting the better of her, 'You've been abroad?
I wondered at the tan. It was too deep to be from a
month in sunny Spain. How exciting.'

'Not entirely,' he replied. 'Though it did have its good
points.'

'Like sun and sand and sea and a bevy of beautiful
women?' she asked.

'Like a lot of hard work despite the exotic settings,' Chase corrected. 'I had a living to earn, believe it or not.'

'Creating concrete jungles for unsuspecting tourists?' Melanie needled.

'No, Melanie. As a matter of fact, I didn't. That would have been the quickest way of making myself a fortune, but I couldn't do that. I take a pride in my work.'

'So what exactly did you do?' she asked, poking with her finger at the stonework, working loose a piece of cement and watching as it dropped into the water, the ripples spreading out in a series of concentric circles before petering out, leaving the surface of the canal calm but for the darting dragon-flies.

'Designed hotels—good hotels,' he stressed. 'Leisure complexes, holiday villages, that sort of thing.'

'In Europe?'

'Sometimes. Portugal, Yugoslavia, but mostly further afield—the US for a time, the Caribbean, Bermuda, other more remote islands.'

'The playgrounds of the idle rich,' Melanie observed with more than a hint of bitterness.

Bermuda. The memories flooded back. Lauren, laughing on the beach, young and slim and golden-brown, hair bleached almost white from the sun; Lauren, dressed to impress, the centre of attraction, the honey-pot around which the drones had buzzed, vying for a smile, a kiss, a favour; Lauren in those last few moments, face released from pain—excitement and wonder and tenderness shining through her eyes; Lauren dead. Too young to die. Too young to die. And then the bombshell, Jack's bombshell, that awful ultimatum.

The sob rose up, catching in her throat, choking her, and Melanie twisted round, jumping off the parapet, squeezing back tears. She crossed over the bridge, leaning against the brickwork, fighting for control, her breath coming in short, sharp gasps.

'Melanie? What's wrong? For God's sake, Melanie, talk to me.'

A hand on her arm, a voice in her ear, a face at her side, concern furrowing his brow. He stood with her, holding her gently, till the nightmare faded, like the ripples in the water, faded, for now. Unlike the ripples in the water the nightmare would return, in the dark hours of the night when she was alone.

'All right?' Chase asked when her colour had returned to something resembling normal.

She nodded, not trusting herself to meet his eyes, acutely aware of his hands on her shoulders, his body close to hers. She made a huge effort to pull herself together.

'Why work abroad?' she asked eventually, gently removing herself from the confines of his arms. 'What made you choose to go away?'

'I didn't,' he replied, eyes searching her face, looking for answers Melanie was not prepared to give. He seemed to sense her mood and nodded, falling into step beside her, jacket tossed nonchalantly over his shoulder.

'There were family problems,' he began, as if seeking to divert her. 'My mother died and my stepfather, who'd never liked me, decided to interpret my mother's last wishes his own way. I was out on my heels, literally. If I didn't prove myself he'd make sure I didn't get a single penny. I didn't have the funds to fight him and so I went. He gave me five years. If I'd made my first million by then I could have the lot. There was no way I could do it over here; he had too many people in his pocket, too much influence. I had to get away, right away. Besides,

I reminded him of my mother. He hated me, hated me for the life in me, the very breath I drew. I was so like her, you see, I don't suppose he could look at me without seeing her eyes, her smile, without hearing her voice. And when I'd made my first million I came home. I expected my inheritance. I was wrong.'

'He wouldn't hand it over?' Melanie asked, intrigued at the sudden insight into his background and, more importantly, the workings of his mind.

'He wouldn't hand it over,' Chase derided, the grating sound at odds with the warm afternoon. 'He laughed at me. He'd tied everything up so tightly that I didn't stand a cat in hell's chance of getting it. Not that I needed the money, not by then. It was the principle that mattered. He'd cheated me.'

'And there was nothing you could do?' Melanie enquired, the first stirrings of sympathy beginning to colour her view of him.

'Legally, no. But there's more than one way to kill a cat, my dear.' He smiled, eyes cold, colourless, lips an ugly snarl, and, walking at his side, Melanie shivered, suddenly chilled despite the heat. 'I'll get even one day,' he continued, voice little more than a whisper. 'I can play him at his own game now, and I'll have my revenge, believe me, Melanie; I'll have my revenge.'

They walked on in silence, each preoccupied, deep in thought. Melanie's mind was racing, a mass of jumbled thoughts, pictures flashing inside her head; a word, a gesture, the smouldering hatred burning in a man's heart.

So that's what drives him, she mused, glancing at the uncompromising profile. No wonder he refuses to take no for an answer. He's a man with a quest, a grail, and it doesn't matter who or what is sacrificed along the way. What Chase Banister wants, Chase Banister is determined to have. She shivered, realising for the first time that by standing in the way of such single-minded ambition she was placing herself right in the firing line. And, with her flimsy defences, did she really stand a chance of holding out against him?

'Come and have a drink,' he urged as they reached the car park. 'A long, cold drink and then I'll take you home. Come on,' he insisted. 'You're still pale. I'm used to the heat and even I'm flagging.'

Melanie glanced at her watch. Four o'clock. She had plenty of time. Suzanne was picking Ben up. He and Jonathan had football practice after school, so he wasn't due home for a while yet. She nodded her agreement and then found a shady corner while Chase was at the bar.

'There's brandy in yours. You looked as if you needed it,' he explained as Melanie took a long, long sip of ice-cold Coke and grimaced at the unexpected taste. 'Sorry. I should have asked first. You might not even like brandy.'

'I love brandy. And thanks.' She smiled. 'I couldn't put my finger on the flavour. I thought it might be some newfangled drink, like cherry cola or dandelion-and-burdock cola. They keep coming up with such fantastic flavours—the mind boggles at what might come next.'

'Brandy cola might take off,' he agreed. 'If I were in the soft drinks business I could be halfway to another million with that one.'

'Is that what's important, making your next million?' Melanie asked. 'Don't you want something else out of life?'

'Like what, for instance? A wife, a family, a nice suburban semi with my slippers and my pipe and my three weeks a year in Benidorm? There's a whole world out there, Melanie, just waiting to be conquered. You only get one invitation to the party of life and I'm determined I'll accept it.'

'Money isn't everything,' she informed him, sucking on an ice-cube.

'Maybe not,' Chase agreed. 'But it helps. It helps to pay the bills, helps to sweeten the more unpleasant aspects of life, it opens a lot of doors.'

'But it doesn't buy you happiness,' she told him softly, waiting for a reaction.

He turned the full force of his gaze on her, eyes dancing with amber lights, amused. 'No, but it damn well helps. Show me a beggar who's happy, really happy, and I'll join him.'

'Would you?' she asked. 'I doubt it. Besides, you're missing my point.'

'Which is?' he enquired politely.

'You can't buy the sun and sand and sea and the birds and the flowers. Oh, yes—I know you could go out tomorrow and purchase an island in the middle of the Pacific that has everything I've mentioned, but you haven't bought them, not really. You've bought space, the space to enjoy them. But I can enjoy them here, today, every day. The poor man at the gates of the palace can enjoy them today, tomorrow, all the tomorrows. Rich or poor, we're surrounded by things that can give us happiness. Happiness isn't a commodity on the world market, happiness is a gift.' And the uncomplicated love of a six-year-old boy, she added to herself, never ceasing to be glad that she had it.

'Maybe you're right, my dear,' Chase mocked. 'But I'm not taking any chances. And at the end of the day I'll be laughing all the way to the bank. It's my in-

surance, Melanie. It might not buy me your definition
of Utopia, but it will buy me what I want.'

Melanie shrugged. He was laughing at her, but it didn't
matter. He lived in a different world, a harsher world,
a more materialistic world. If that was what he wanted,
well, it was a free country. She wasn't rich, not in his
sense. But she had so much more in her life that she
could even feel sorry for him. Poor little rich boy, a
mother's pampered darling. He had so much and yet
nothing, nothing at all. And he didn't even know it. And
how he'd laugh if he could read her mind.

'You know something?' Chase said when they were
halfway home. 'You're the most unusual woman I've
ever met.'

'Didn't I tell you I was special when we set out?'
Melanie countered, warming at the unexpected praise.

'It doesn't do to believe everything you're told. And
I hardly knew you then. I've had a few hours to form
an opinion and I'm impressed, Melanie, very impressed.
Do you realise, I've practically told you my life story?
There are people who've known me for years who know
less about me than you do. And what do I know about
you? Nothing, nothing at all. Just the same bare facts
that I knew yesterday, or last week or last month. Oh,
I know where you live, how you fill your time; I now
know what you look like, how you dress, can hazard a
guess at your sense of humour, but, apart from that,
I'm completely in the dark.'

'What's there to know?' Melanie asked, watching his
profile, her eyes tracing the outline of his cruel, aquiline
nose, the square, determined chin.

'You tell me,' he countered, turning his head for an
instant, eyes locking with hers, challenging, enquiring.

She lowered her gaze, flushing under his scrutiny. There was nothing she could tell, nothing he would understand. The past was complex and painful, the hurt too raw to share with someone like him. What was he but a passing stranger? Here today, tomorrow gone, never to return.

'No dark and distant secrets?' he teased. 'No skeletons hiding in the cupboard? You're an enigma, so obviously self-contained, and yet I sense something, something deep and important. Most intriguing, fascinating in fact. I'd love to climb inside your head and see what makes you tick.'

'You'd probably be very bored,' she replied lightly, glad they were almost home. He hadn't struck her as a sensitive man, but his last few comments had come far too close for comfort.

They pulled up outside the cottage as Suzanne's Metro appeared from the opposite direction.

'It looks like you've got visitors,' Chase observed, opening the passenger door and helping her out.

'No, it's just Ben,' Melanie replied completely without thinking and raising her hand to the small boy scrambling out before the car had barely stopped.

'Ben?' Chase queried lightly, eyebrows rising in surprise. 'Not the irate boyfriend? You didn't mention a man in your life. How remiss of you, Melanie.'

'Oh, no,' she protested. 'You've got it all wrong. Ben's my——'

'Mummy! Mummy!' shouted the child, launching himself the last few yards and tumbling headlong into Melanie's outstretched arms, cutting short her explanation.

She glanced up. Chase was quick, but not quite quick enough. The shock registered in his eyes, shock and fleeting condemnation, and then the shutters came down and he returned her gaze unblinking.

Melanie's heart sank. He'd done what people always did, jumped to the obvious conclusion. Was it his fault that he'd got it wrong?

thing. I'm sure he'll be in touch. And when he does I'll share that new-found faith in the male populace. Just now the candle's burning too low to see by.' She broke off, unabashed at the quizzical ceilings of Melanie's expression. 'What's that you were going to say, Suzanne? Was it . . .'

CHAPTER THREE

'YOU'RE a sly one,' Suzanne needled half an hour later when Chase had finally driven off. 'How long have you been keeping him to yourself? Come on, Melanie, you can tell me. Discretion's my middle name.'

Melanie coloured, but laughed at her friend's speculative expression. 'You've got it all wrong,' she told her. 'I can see the scenario rolling in your eyes, but you're wrong, Suzanne. He's just a man, not even a friend. This time yesterday we'd barely met. This time tomorrow he'll probably be two hundred miles away and that will be the last we see of him. At least, that's what I'm hoping.'

'Oh, yes? And who do you think you're kidding?' Suzanne mocked, sipping her coffee. 'He isn't going anywhere, at least not for a while. I saw the way he looked at you. He's interested, Melanie, very interested. I'd lay money on his sticking around for a while yet.'

Melanie shrugged. 'Sure,' she replied, sugaring her drink, stirring the spoon slowly, thoughtfully around her cup. 'He's young, good-looking, filthy rich. Just the sort of man who wastes his time on Little Miss Nobody from the provinces. It's a nice idea, Suzanne, but you can stop planning the wedding, the bedding and the christening of the children. Chase wants something from me all right but it's none of the things you're hoping.'

'I wouldn't be too sure of that,' Suzanne continued, speculation still beaming from her eyes. 'He doesn't strike me as the sort of man who wastes time on anything. If Chase is still here tomorrow—and I'll wager that he is—then you're the point of interest, not the cottage.'

'And how do you work that one out?' Melanie asked, secretly warming at the words but not about to let the thought show on her face.

'Simple, Melanie. He's a businessman, and business these days can be conducted halfway across the world at the touch of a button. He'll have heard of telephones, fax machines, communication systems. He no more needs to be here than I need to travel to the moon for a holiday. He's curious, Melanie, intrigued. You've kept him dangling for the past three months, not the sort of treatment a man of his calibre expects. He's used to success, expects it, buys it if necessary. And, when he comes up against a brick wall, he knocks it down. Unless of course the brick wall turns out to be young, female and somewhat attractive.'

Melanie shrugged again, the blush rising in her cheeks. 'You may be right,' she agreed solemnly, deliberately avoiding her friend's knowing eye. 'But I don't think so. In any case, he's wasting his time. He might be used to susceptible females swooning at his feet the moment he raises his little finger, but I'm not about to be bowled over. It takes more than an obscene bank-balance and a pair of laughing brown eyes to influence me. He's just another man, and men, Suzanne, simply don't register on my list of priorities. There's only one man in my life and that's how I aim to keep it. He's six years old, he loves me and needs me and is totally and utterly uncomplicated.'

'But there's no fun in your life,' Suzanne protested. 'You can't go on forever holding men at arm's length. You should be going out, enjoying yourself. You're still young, Melanie. You should be seizing life by the horns, not stagnating, letting life pass you by, continuing to punish yourself for something that happened six or seven years ago. Ben's a well-adjusted kid; he could cope with a bit of competition for your time and affection.'

'You forget, my matchmaking friend, Chase Banister is just passing through. He isn't going to be around long enough for anyone to get to know. Ben needs stability, not a succession of brash young men with only one thing on their minds.'

Suzanne snorted in derision. 'That's nonsense and you know it. Ben's never had the chance. You've been keeping men at bay for as long as I've known you. There should be men in your life, in Ben's life. You're not being fair to either of you, living the life of a nun. I could understand it if you were middle-aged, but, damn it all, Melanie, twenty-six is hardly over the hill.'

'I'm happy enough,' Melanie protested, recognising Suzanne's concern and touched by it. 'And that's how I'd like it to stay. You and Tony may be happy together, but not everyone's as well suited as you, as lucky as you. Can't you see? It's too much hit and miss. I can't risk being hurt, Suzanne, not again, and for Ben's sake too, as well as my own. I've tried so hard not to turn bitter and I think I've succeeded. Think what would happen if I allowed myself to get involved and then discovered I'd made a bad choice.'

'Just now I'd be happy to see you make any choice. Didn't you enjoy your lunch, the company, the *male* company?' Suzanne asked, draining her cup and replacing it in the saucer.

'Yes, but——'

'Yes but nothing. You did it. Don't you see? You actually went out with a man, you know, that alien species who make up roughly fifty per cent of the human race. If you can do it once, you can do it again. Promise me you will, the next time he asks you.'

'Some hope,' Melanie told her ruefully. 'I saw his face when Ben came running. This might be the nineteen-nineties but the double standards are still firmly in place.'

'You mean you didn't tell him?'

Melanie raised an eyebrow. 'Oh, yes, I'm really into pouring out my heart to perfect strangers over chicken *cacciatora* and noodles,' she reprimanded with gentle sarcasm.

'He won't be, if you give him half a chance. And he will ask again, I feel it in my bones.'

'You and your feelings,' Melanie scoffed. 'You'll be reading my tea-leaves next, coming up with wonderful predictions about tall, dark and handsome strangers inexplicably linked with wedding bells.'

'Ah! So you admit that he's handsome!' Suzanne exclaimed gleefully. 'That's promising.'

'Nothing of the sort,' Melanie protested, colouring. 'Of course he's handsome. I'd need to be blind not to notice, but don't build up your hopes, my dear. I'm immune, and that's how I intend it to stay.'

'Famous last words,' Suzanne warned with a very knowing smile. 'You could be sorry you ever said that, in another week or two. You see if I'm wrong.'

Three days later Melanie was beginning to suspect that Suzanne was right—about some things at least.

Chase was still around, his voice on the phone each evening sending little shivers of excitement running through her. Melanie held her ground, determined to keep him at arm's length, aware of danger on two fronts and not about to allow him close enough to pierce her defences. He was a clever man, but Melanie held the upper hand. She had something he wanted and as long as she didn't make any stupid mistakes he could never come near enough to wheedle it from her. She didn't want him for a friend, and she didn't want him for a lover, and she knew instinctively that he was capable of being both if he thought it would further his cause. She'd seen too many lives ruined to satisfy the demands of men like Chase and she wasn't about to add her own scalp to the pile.

Monday dawned bright and sunny, the cloudless sky promising a continuation of the warm spell, and Melanie walked Ben to school, picking Jonathan up on the way. She stopped to chat at the school gates, exchanging gossip with other young mums before ambling home, revelling in the luxury of having nothing at all to do for once. The day was hers. She would tidy up, run the vacuum cleaner quickly over the carpets, and then spend the day in the garden with a book. Peace and quiet and solitude. Sheer bliss. And another of those best-laid plans.

Chase was waiting on the step when she got home, the BMW parked outside the gate advertising his presence as she rounded the final bend.

Melanie halted, the breath leaving her body as she took in the significance of the gleaming blue car. She should have known, deep down she had known, just hadn't wanted to believe it. They'd played this game before and the rules hadn't changed. But, in a way, that was her advantage.

Gathering her wits, she strode purposefully forward, planting a smile on her face as she pushed open the front gate.

'Good morning, Chase. Isn't it a beautiful day?' she trilled, as if finding his presence there a perfectly normal occurrence.

'Good morning, Melanie. It certainly is,' he agreed, uncurling his long legs and standing up to greet her.

'You're up and about early,' she commented. 'Not on your way home, by any chance?'

Chase smiled broadly, triggering another shock reaction deep inside her as the hard lines of his face relaxed and the amber eyes, dancing with light, focused their knowing gaze on hers.

'Wishful thinking?' he teased softly. 'Sorry to have to disappoint you, but no, Melanie, I'm not on my way home. I've no intention of going home, not yet, not until I get the answer I want, the answer I need. The ball's in your court now. Just say the word and I'll be gone, out of your hair for good. I'll make it worth your while.'

'Wrong, Chase. There isn't enough money in this world to make it worth my while. I'm not selling. End of discussion.'

'End of discussion for *now*,' he informed her. 'I've not given up. You'll come round, sooner or later.'

'I wouldn't bank on it,' Melanie retorted, and, pointedly inserting her key in the lock, 'Now, if you'll excuse me, I am rather busy.'

'Too busy for a cup of coffee?' he asked. 'Or is that your excuse? Frightened, Melanie? Of me? Surely not,' he mocked. 'You can hold your own, unless I've seriously misjudged you.'

'Don't they serve coffee at your hotel?' she asked, flushing with annoyance.

'They do indeed,' he told her. 'And very good coffee at that. But the company's not very sparkling.'

'It isn't very sparkling here, either,' she snapped, 'but I don't suppose that's going to stop you. It's only instant,' she warned, opening the door and stepping over the threshold.

'Instant will be lovely.'

He seemed to fill her tiny lounge, stretching out on the settee and totally dominating the room. He picked up the morning paper and idly thumbed through it while Melanie thankfully escaped to the kitchen. She took her time, aware that she was stalling, but determined to remain in control, determined to stay cool, calm and collected in his presence.

She added a plateful of biscuits to the tray and carried it through, placing it on the coffee-table, taking the chair opposite, watching him from beneath lowered lashes. He seemed perfectly at home, perfectly relaxed, not even needing the noise of inconsequential small talk as the silence lengthened.

He finished his drink and replaced the cup in the saucer, and then looked up and across at her so intently that Melanie felt the blush creep into her cheeks.

'Have dinner with me tonight,' he said, eyes holding hers.

'I'm sorry, I can't,' Melanie replied, heart beginning to beat erratically in her breast.

'Otherwise engaged?' he asked. 'Or just washing your hair?'

'No baby-sitter,' she told him promptly, and then waited while he digested her hastily formed pretext.

'Not even Suzanne?' he asked. 'Another friend? Someone's teenage daughter? There must be someone you know who could sit for a couple of hours.'

'Not a soul,' Melanie told him, completely untruthfully and not a bit repentant. Many were the nights Ben had slept at Suzanne's. It was the perfect solution and one she had been able to reciprocate on other occasions. But she wasn't about to tell Chase that. Keep him at arm's length, girl, she was telling herself, close him down. He'll give up eventually, crawl away with his tail between his legs. And you'll have won, girl, you'll have won. She returned his gaze unblinking, face composed while she waited for his next move.

'Tomorrow, then? Or any night. I'm not going anywhere for a while and my social calendar's probably less cluttered than yours. You decide when you can make it. I'm completely at your disposal.'

'Are you always so obliging?' Melanie asked, racking her brains for a suitable excuse. She could always just say no, of course, but she didn't want to seem rude, not unless she had to.

'No, young lady, I am not. But for you I'll make an exception.'

'Honoured, aren't I?' she found herself teasing. 'Would it seem exceedingly ungracious if I declined?'

'Exceedingly,' he agreed solemnly. 'But that isn't going to stop you. Is it my aftershave, my deodorant, or the way I cut my hair?'

'None of those, as I'm sure you know, but it's difficult with Ben. I can't just get up and go at the drop of a hat.'

'You know, tact is one of those virtues I've never understood,' he told her. 'No is still no, no matter how prettily you wrap it up. But I suppose I should be flattered. If you really disliked me you'd have given your favourite answer. Thanks, but no, thanks, is how you usually phrase it.'

'There, you see? I'm boringly predictable. I've done you a favour, if only you could see it, saved you from a night of tedium over the flickering candles.'

'And condemned me instead to a night of tedium watching TV in a hotel bedroom.'

'You're pulling at my heart-strings, Chase,' she mocked.

'Cruel lady. Have you no heart? Have you no pity for a lonely man, a stranger in this county?'

'You could always go back to London,' she suggested slyly.

'I could indeed. But it's a long way to go for dinner and I like it here. The people are so friendly, so obliging. At least, most of them are. You must be the exception that proves the rule.'

'There's no shortage of pretty girls in town,' she countered.

'True. But then, they're not all endowed with your vivacity, your wit, your ability to make a man feel welcome. Tell me something,' he ended, suddenly turning serious.

'If I can,' Melanie replied, instantly wary.

'What's the real reason? You enjoyed lunch on Thursday, or at least I think you did. Why not dinner?'

'Why not leave it at thanks, Chase, but no, thanks? Does there have to be an inquest?'

He shrugged, standing up, head dangerously close to the ceiling. 'Let's say I'm mildly curious.'

'Not used to the cold shoulder?' Melanie needled, getting to her feet and leading the way to the front door.

'It's against the rules,' Chase told her. 'Hitting a man when he's down.'

'You'll bounce back,' she countered cheerfully.

'No thanks to you. Thanks for the coffee and the sparkling conversation, and, if you do change your mind, the offer remains open. I'm staying at the Cedar Tree.'

'Don't stay in on my account,' Melanie warned.

'If I stay in,' he informed her coldly, 'then it's for the same reason I do most things. In short, because I want to. I'll be seeing you. And Melanie,' he added, having started off down the path but halting and turning, face impassive, eyes devoid of light as they travelled the length of her before finally settling on her face, 'that's definitely a promise.'

'Hi.'

Melanie glanced up from her book. 'Hi to you,' she replied, the blood rushing to her cheeks as she made a vain effort to control her emotions. She scowled. She hoped he wasn't going to spoil another day, stirring up emotions she'd rather leave buried, feelings she wasn't yet ready to admit to, feelings that left her restless, spoiled her concentration, seemed inextricably focused on the finely chiselled features of the six-foot two-inch form towering over her, eyes gently mocking, the now familiar lazy smile playing about the corners of his mouth.

The longer he stayed around the more she found herself agreeing with Suzanne. Melanie could be the point of interest, a means to an end, if the truth was known. Offering more money wasn't working, and, since Chase was determined to have his own way, he'd changed his tactics, changed his rules, was feigning an interest in Melanie herself. And, given his obvious attraction, why not? He was probably used to women swooning at his feet the moment he crooked his little finger. But not this time, Melanie told herself sternly, scowl deepening, not this time.

'Another welcome fit for kings,' Chase observed sardonically as Melanie made no move to get up from the sun-lounger. 'Much more of this and I'll be going home with a complex.'

'Home?' Melanie asked, the resultant jolt in the pit of her stomach shocking in its intensity.

'There you go again,' he teased. 'Building up your hopes. I expect I'll go home eventually, but just now I'm more than happy here. Come for a drive,' he suggested. 'And no excuses about being too busy and the shortage of baby-sitters and the hundred and one other reasons you're capable of dredging up in an instant. Today, madam, I refuse to take no for an answer.'

'Very masterful,' she mocked, beginning to get herself in hand and returning his gaze unflinchingly. 'What happens when I call your bluff?'

'Want to wait and find out?' he asked, a dangerous edge to his voice as he took a step nearer.

Melanie shook her head. 'I guess not,' she conceded, common sense prevailing—just.

'Pity,' he commented, smile widening. 'It could have been fun.'

'Shall I change?' Melanie asked, ignoring his words and the gleam in his eye.

Chase shook his head. 'You're perfect as you are,' he insisted. 'Where shall we go?'

'What had you in mind?' she asked, following him up the garden path, slamming shut the front door on the way.

'Nothing special,' Chase replied, helping her into the car. 'Just a couple of hours in the company of a fair maiden, a picnic by a river or a stream so we can dangle our feet in the water, a glass or two of ice-cold wine over strawberries and cream, and a leisurely stroll hand in hand with only the birds for company. Sound tempting?'

'Some of it,' Melanie retorted. 'But we're not very well endowed with rivers or fair maidens who fall for a silver tongue. Lancashire lasses are apt to be a bit more down to earth. However, if I'll do—a very poor second best, I'm sure—I promise to enjoy the strawberries, and I might even manage the leisurely stroll—side by side and about six feet apart. Want to change your mind?' she asked, slipping him a sideways glance.

'Lady,' he retorted, lips twitching in amusement, 'you drive a real hard bargain. It wasn't quite what I had in mind, but I'll take it. Who knows? Things might go my way yet.'

'And then again,' she couldn't resist chiding, 'they might not.'

They drove out to Parbold Hill, an easy ride through hedgerowed lanes and sleepy villages, and parked right at the top where they could drink in the view and Melanie could point out the landmarks.

The usual place for a picnic was the beach, but Melanie wasn't exactly enamoured of the sand-encrusted food which tended to result when she took Ben out for the day. Besides, beaches conjured up visions of swimsuits and scantily clad bodies, and she didn't want to make herself any more vulnerable than she already was.

'It's amazing, looking out over all this to think of the mill towns and industry just a few miles to the east,' Chase observed as they perched themselves on a tumble-down wall and gazed down at the valley they had left behind.

'And Liverpool twelve miles thataway, not to mention Wigan a bit closer to home,' Melanie replied, hugging her knees to her body. It wasn't cold out but they were high and exposed, and the slight breeze caught at her bare arms and legs, raising goose-pimples.

'It's a changing region,' he continued. 'Stereotyped ideas of the coal towns and the mill towns and the grim port of Liverpool are totally out of date. It's an area with a lot of potential, a lot of potential indeed.'

'And is that why you're here?' Melanie asked, turning her head to look at him. 'To exploit that potential?'

'Not exploit, Melanie,' Chase corrected. 'Utilise.'

'Oh? And is there a difference?' she found herself asking.

'You know there is. Progress doesn't have to be destructive, Melanie. My developments are always well thought-out, well planned, tailor-made for the local community, but you don't have to take my word for that. Check them out for yourself.'

'I might just do that,' she retorted, slipping off the wall and beginning to amble back to where they'd left the car.

'I hope you do,' he told her seriously, falling into step. 'You might even approve. Not that I'm holding out much hope.'

'And would that bother you?' she asked, conscious of him at her side, a lot closer than the six feet she'd laughingly stipulated before they'd set out.

'Ordinarily no,' he replied. 'I don't need approval, anyone's approval. I believe in myself entirely and utterly and I've never been wrong yet.'

'You won't need me patting you on the head, then.'

'No, but I do need you to see sense.'

'Like signing away my home so you can bulldoze it into oblivion?'

'It's a reasonable offer, Melanie, more than reasonable. You wouldn't get the kind of money I'm offering off anyone else.'

'Keep your money, Chase. I'm not interested.'

'So you keep saying. But it doesn't make sense. Not to me.' He halted suddenly, turning towards her, forcing her to stop. 'You don't believe all that tripe about tearing up roots any more than I do. A home is what you make it, a warm, loving, family environment, not just a heap of bricks and mortar. You've the whole town to choose from. Do yourself a favour. Pick another home, create another home for you and Ben. I'll make it worth your while.'

'No.'

'Why not?' he demanded, reaching out, gripping her shoulders. 'Tell me, Melanie.'

At the touch of his fingers Melanie went weak. She closed her eyes, blocking out his face, inwardly fighting for control. It didn't help that he was right, that he *was* being generous in his offer. But she couldn't sell. Even if she wanted to, how could she? Hilary had left her the cottage, had wanted Melanie to have it, had openly disapproved of the large-scale developments Chase was involved with. She'd trusted Melanie. How could Melanie betray that trust now, leaving the way clear for Chase to turn the estate into the one thing Hilary would never have allowed?

'Tell me,' he insisted, shaking her slightly, forcing Melanie to open her eyes.

'You wouldn't understand,' she murmured, trying to avoid his piercing glance.

'Try me.'

'No.'

'Don't be stubborn, Melanie. I want to know, I need to know.'

'No!'

'Why on earth not?' he asked, less in anger than in mild exasperation.

'Because you wouldn't understand,' she repeated, raising her chin in defiance. 'You wouldn't understand.'

'You really are an obstinate, wilful, pig-headed sort of woman,' he observed, continuing to pin her with his eyes.

'Just a match for an obstinate, wilful, pig-headed sort of man,' Melanie replied with feeling.

There was a loaded pause, a fraction of a second while her words sank in, and then his face changed, eyes darkening, smouldering, mouth curving in a satisfied, sensual smile.

Melanie stood very still, every fibre of her body taut and strained as the air around them crackled with emotion, electricity flowing tangibly between them.

'You know,' Chase drawled, moving nearer, sliding his hands down her arms and cupping her elbows, 'I'm beginning to think you might just be right.'

The result was electric, his fingers burning into her, and Melanie twisted away, trying to jerk free, her movements futile as the hands tightened their grip. Chase shook his head, a light, admonishing gesture, and tugged her even closer, shocking her again as the tense muscles of his thighs came up against her own. Melanie gasped as his hands slid under her hair, fingers gliding over naked skin, soothing and searing at the same time; the most delicate of movements and yet each and every one an indelible brand.

'It's there, Melanie,' he told her, voice low and urgent. 'You can fight it if you want, but the spark is there. I can feel it and so can you,' he insisted, the amber glow of his eyes pouring over her, bathing her with light.

'I don't know what you mean,' she lied, voice not quite steady.

'Yes, you do,' he purred huskily. 'I'm sure you know. You're responding, Melanie. I can see it in your face, feel the fluttering beneath my fingers. Your body's betrayed you, *this* has betrayed you.' He brushed the pulse-spot in her neck, his fingers stroking, stirring her response while Melanie stood transfixed, her eyes drowning in his, her body trembling beneath his touch.

Far, far away someone else was speaking. It couldn't happen, the voice was saying deep inside her head. It isn't possible, not like this. And yet it had, Melanie realised. In less than an instant the carefully constructed fabric of her life had crumbled, been swept away, stripping her bare, leaving her vulnerable. In the time taken to draw breath her tenacious hold on common sense had slipped irretrievably as everything life had stood for dissolved in her mind, dissolved and drifted away, re-formed with this man at the centre. She gazed into his eyes, uncertainty, fear, dawning wonder shadowing her face.

'I'm going to kiss you,' Chase crooned, the words filling her ears, exciting, thrilling. 'But before I kiss you, Melanie, I need to know if that's what you want too. You *do* want me to kiss you, don't you, Melanie, don't you?'

But Melanie was mesmerised, robbed of coherent thought, her brain incapable of forming any words, and though her mouth opened slightly it was simply to allow a nervous tongue to moisten dry lips, the darting pink tip unknowingly inviting.

Chase shuddered and groaned from somewhere deep inside, gathering Melanie to him, and then his mouth was on hers, demanding, bruising, exploring.

Instinct took over as Melanie swayed in his arms, her hands moving automatically, *naturally*, to the nape of his neck, her fingers twining in the massed silkiness of his hair, urging his mouth down on hers, pushing her body into the straining lines of his.

Melanie, too, groaned as the kiss deepened, her tongue exploring his mouth, loving the taste of him, the feel of him, the magic of his touch as his hands moved upwards, slipping under her T-shirt, fingers gliding over her bare skin, stroking her quivering flesh, brushing and stroking again, moving up her back, moulding her to him.

And still his mouth never left hers, still his tongue continued to dart between her lips, reaching for her tongue, each moment of contact sending darts of pleasure rippling through her.

When finally they drew apart a little it was their eyes that locked, Chase's deep and dark and serious, Melanie's troubled sapphire pools reflecting all her inner turmoil, her wonderment, her hope.

Chase smiled, turning her heart over, and brought a hand up to her cheek, his thumb tracing the outline of her jaw, sending shivers of desire racing through her again.

'You're so beautiful,' he murmured hoarsely. 'So very, very beautiful.' And they stood together, Melanie's head on his shoulder, Chase's arms around her, holding her close until their breathing quietened and their racing hearts returned to normal.

A lifetime passed and then Chase tilted her chin, his eyes seeking answers in hers, and Melanie held her breath as he dipped his head, touching her lips with his own briefly, too briefly, the momentary contact shocking her again.

'Come on,' he said, sliding his hand down her arm until their fingers entwined and locked. 'Let's go and eat.'

It was a strange meal, in a hollow on the hillside, sheltered from the gentle breeze by the curving sides of a natural depression which gave them privacy, seclusion, an isolated intimacy. Melanie barely tasted the beautifully prepared food Chase laid out on the rug. There was cold chicken and salad, cooked meats and quiche, cartons of rice delicately spicy, and exotic vegetables in vinaigrette and mayonnaise. The bread was crusty, topped with poppy seeds and sesame seeds and spread with soft golden butter, and they ate with their fingers, pulling the food gently apart, licking fingers clean in highly erotic manner which kept Melanie's nerves stretched taut as her eyes returned time and again to his, sought reassurance in his.

Finally came the strawberries, and as Melanie's hand reached out for a spoon Chase pushed it out of reach, gently shaking his head, and Melanie watched, fascinated, as he took hold of a piece of fruit, dipped it first in his glass of Chablis, and then offered it silently to her to take. She opened her mouth, taking the fruit, and as she swallowed, eyes never leaving his face, she reached out, reciprocating, her fingers brushing his lips as he took the ripe berry from her.

When they had finished and the debris had been cleared they sat together on the rug, hand in hand, not speaking, and Melanie rested her head on his shoulder, closed her eyes, imagined herself in paradise. It was magical, incredible, a million miles from reality and she never, ever wanted it to end.

Glancing up, she found his eyes on her, solemn and intense, and her heart turned over, misreading their message, but even as she pulled away another arm came out to hold her, to draw her back, and the expression softened as Chase smiled, his eyes travelling the length of her body and back again, coming to rest on her face.

His hands cupped her face and he lowered his head to kiss her again, rekindling the fire in Melanie's heart. 'I'm going to make love to you,' he told her hoarsely, lowering her gently down on to the rug. 'And I'm going to love each and every moment, *you're* going to love each and every moment. We're alone, Melanie, just you and me, man and woman, a million miles from anywhere, and I want you, I want you.'

His hands slipped under her flimsy T-shirt, stroking her taut flesh, and Melanie came alive at his touch, moving her body under his fingers. His eyes were boring into hers, desire reflected, one from the other, mirrors within mirrors, the message quivering on the air.

'You're so beautiful, so very beautiful,' he rasped, 'but I want all of you, Melanie, I want to see all of you. You do understand, don't you, my love?' He didn't wait for an answer, didn't need one. Melanie's eyes were smoky with passion, her lips swollen, stained with fruit, deliciously inviting, and she held her breath as he pushed the T-shirt up and above her shoulders, tugging it easily over her head, his gaze moving from her eyes to her breasts and back again.

He reached out, snapping open the front fastening of her bra, and as her breasts spilled out she heard the sudden sharp intake of his breath.

'You're an incredible woman,' he murmured huskily. 'In my wildest dreams I never imagined you'd be so beautiful, that your body could be like this. My God, you're so beautiful.'

Melanie writhed as his hand travelled the length of her, following the curves and undulations, and she arched her body to prolong the contact.

'Not yet,' Chase whispered, the slow, intimate smile tugging at her heart. 'You're not ready yet. I want you to enjoy every moment, so relax, Melanie, relax.'

He kissed her again, lightly, enticingly, his fingers reaching out for her breasts, closing round them, kneading, teasing, lifting her higher and ever higher, drawing out responses she hadn't known existed. She was alive! For the first time in her life she was truly alive, all her senses honed and sharpened, primed to receive the pleasure only Chase could give.

He stretched out beside her, his lips raining kisses across her cheeks then down to the hollow in her throat, where he lingered a moment before starting another journey, lower, nearer, so near and yet so far, circling each breast but still not touching, tantalising, coming nearer, infinitely nearer, and yet denying Melanie the satisfaction she craved. Her body moved under his mouth, signalling her need, and still he denied her, still he skirted her aching breasts, the straining nipples, until Melanie was ready to explode with bitter-sweet frustration.

'Please, Chase,' she moaned, unable to bear the suspense any longer.

He smiled, a lazy, sultry smile, and then paused, eyes locking with hers, hands quiescent on her body. 'Ready now?' he asked. 'Yes, of course you are. I knew you'd enjoy it. There was ice in your tone and ice in your eyes but underneath that was fire waiting to be kindled. All it needed was the right man, Melanie, the right man.'

And as he spoke, eyes never leaving her face, he opened the buttons of his shirt with the slow, deliberate movements of a man still in control, and as he reached the last he shrugged himself out of it, a smile playing about the corners of his mouth, a smile of pleasure, of satisfaction, the smile of a sleek cat after its kill.

He dipped forward, dropping his gaze to her breasts, and when the eye contact severed something snapped as Melanie's mind sobered, jerking her back to reality.

'No!' she rasped, voice torn with anguish as she twisted sideways out of his embrace. 'No, Chase, no!'

But he was quicker than she, his hands on her shoulders, wrenching her back to face him. One cruel hand forced her chin up, forced her to meet that awful, frigid gaze.

'You little bitch,' he hissed, lips twisted into an ugly snarl. 'No one says no to me, Melanie. No one.' His mouth closed on hers, biting, blistering, deliberately in-sulting, deliberately punishing, and then the pressure re-laxed as the lips began persuading, caressing, coaxing a response. And Melanie trembled uncontrollably and knew that she was lost.

CHAPTER FOUR

'WHY?' Chase asked a lifetime later. 'Why?'

Melanie sat and hugged her knees to her body, her eyes bleak, unseeing. The trembling had subsided and now she was cold, cold as ice, though the afternoon sun still beat down from a cloudless sky.

He'd released her immediately, of course, having gained the advantage, striding away and leaving her, and she'd wondered, fleetingly, if he intended to leave her there on the hillside, alone, never so alone. But she'd heard his step some time later, didn't turn her head as he flung himself down on the blanket, legs outstretched, body casually supported on one arm. And the silence drew out between them, seemed never to end.

Melanie was devastated. Everything she had striven for, all her careful control, years of avoiding involvements, of keeping her emotions intact, all gone in the madness of a summer afternoon. How could she? How could she let him creep under her defences, reach to the very heart of her, to her soul? How could she offer herself so cheaply, respond so eagerly to the touch of his fingers and lips? It didn't help that he'd finally rejected her. Even in that she had lost control, had thought she could deny him, but had allowed him his moment of triumph. 'No one says no to me, Melanie,' he had sneered, and then he had proved it, how cruelly he had proved it, and how could she ever look him in the eye again? And how could she live with herself, knowing that she'd come so close to throwing everything away?

For six long years she'd held herself aloof, the pain
of Jack's rejection softened by the uncomplicated love
of the baby. She'd made a vow then, a promise to herself,
and she'd never once wavered, never. She didn't need
men. Men brought trouble, gave nothing in return; first
Lauren falling for a silver tongue, refusing to believe
that the young, rich, fun-loving father of the child she
carried could leave her high and dry, and then Jack, insisting that Ben should be adopted, be given away to
perfect strangers, insisting that Melanie choose between
them. One tiny baby or one grown man; one vulnerable
scrap of humanity or the man she had promised to marry.

She'd known Jack so well, or so she'd thought, remembering the fun they'd had when their long-
established friendship turned to love. He'd showered her
with gifts, chocolates, flowers, sentimental keepsakes,
had wined her and dined her, made her dizzy with the
pace of their social life, packing so much into their time
together. He'd told her that he loved her, had promised
her the moon and the stars, and then brought her down
to earth so cruelly with his flat refusal to consider even
for a moment Melanie's keeping Lauren's baby, bringing
Ben up as their own.

'I don't even like children,' he'd informed her matter-
of-factly. 'I don't want any of my own and I'm most
definitely not prepared to shoulder the responsibility of
someone else's by-blow. No, Melanie, it's perfectly
simple, really; either the baby goes or I go.'

And Melanie hadn't hesitated at all, turning her back
on the easy life, burying the pain but not forgetting the
betrayal, determined never again to let any man come
close enough to touch her heart, to stir her emotions.
And now she'd failed, oh, how she'd failed.

'Is it Ben?' Chase asked when it became apparent that Melanie had no intention of speaking. 'Ben's father? Is that the reason? Did he hurt you, Melanie, leave you, fill your belly with his seed and then desert you? Is that why you froze me out? Do you really think I'm the sort of man who lies with a woman, loves a woman, then leaves her to pick up the pieces? No, don't bother to answer,' he flung out bitterly. 'Of course you do. It's hardly your fault, is it? One man is a bastard, so why not all?'

'It's—a lot more complicated than you'd imagine,' she managed to choke out eventually, the single tear trailing down her cheek unheeded.

'It always is, isn't it?' he sighed. 'Life's always much more complicated than we think. It's half the fun I suppose, threading our way through the tortuous trails of the life-maze, playing the game while the gods look on in amusement, setting traps and pitfalls and laughing when we stumble in. Only you don't want to climb out, do you, Melanie? You've fallen into your bunker and you're going to stay there, because it's safer. You've wrapped yourself up in cotton wool and you're going to sit back and let life pass you by. Such a waste, Melanie, such an awful waste.'

'You don't understand,' she murmured, still gazing straight ahead, her voice low, full of emotion.

'You won't give me the chance to. You came alive, Melanie, I watched you. You sparkled, you dazzled, you pulsated with emotion. You woke yourself up from some deep, deep sleep, and then on the very edge of some momentous step you drew back, settled for safety, settled for second best.'

'It's easy enough to judge from the outside,' she pointed out.

'Then let me in. Let me help. Stop holding me at arm's length.' He spun round, coming to his knees, reaching out, taking hold of her shoulders. 'Tell me, Melanie. Tell me why. Explain why you're doing this to yourself. You're not hurting me or Ben or anyone else. You're hurting yourself. Can't you see?' he demanded, dark eyes boring into hers. 'Can't you see what you're doing? Don't do it, don't let life pass you by. You'll regret it one day, in five or ten or twenty years' time when you wake up and discover you've missed out. It will be too late. Are you listening?' he demanded, shaking her, fingers digging into the flesh of her shoulders, painful reminder of the effect he had on her body. 'One mistake doesn't damn you for all eternity,' he insisted. 'Start living again. For God's sake, Melanie, start living.'

'Why? Why do you care?' she retorted, anger breaking through at last. 'I'm nothing to you, nothing but a plaything. I was happy enough, cocooned in my own world. I had everything I needed till you arrived and started rocking the boat. Why don't you go away and leave me alone? Go back to London, Chase. There's nothing for you here, nothing at all. It's a different world, one you couldn't even begin to understand. And you don't belong, you'll never belong.'

'Perhaps you're right,' he acknowledged bleakly. 'But at least I was trying. But you needn't worry, I've got the message. There are too many other things demanding my attention to waste time on lost causes. Get in the car,' he instructed crisply, standing up, snatching at her wrist and jerking her roughly to her feet. 'It's time we went home.'

Life went on automatically. Melanie's days never varied. Dropping Ben at school, she would return to the cottage and fill the daylight hours with work, work, and more work. The chapters of the book piled up quickly under her nimble fingers, and when the typing was finished there was the garden to attend to, the cottage to clean from top to bottom, carpets to shampoo, curtains to change, windows to wash. Never before had everything looked so clean and tidy and gleaming, and never before had she been forced to live with the huge void Chase's absence left in her heart.

When Lauren died and Jack walked out she'd been much too busy to give in to the misery. Ben had demanded her attention, her patience and her love, had helped her over the dark months. This time there were no distractions. And though the pain shouldn't really have compared, Melanie was achingly aware that it did, and that, if anything, it was worse.

Suzanne, with the understanding born of friendship, did her best to divert her, inviting Melanie and Ben round to supper, accompanying Melanie to the cinema and local plays, evenings at the theatre in Liverpool and Manchester, filling the hours between late afternoon and bedtime; but the dark hours of the night when Ben slept soundly and Melanie was completely and utterly alone were the hours that crept by like years, were the times she dreaded. And yet in the cold light of day she could look back and wonder what had happened to destroy her peace of mind. It was only an afternoon. A few hours with a man, giving and receiving pleasure, a few hours spoiled by Melanie's determination not to get involved. Ridiculous, really. The twenty-first century was rapidly appearing on the horizon and yet modern Melanie Sandford couldn't lie in a man's arms without panicking, couldn't forgive herself for letting him arouse her, couldn't forgive herself—and this one took a lot of facing—for denying them both the natural conclusion to their actions. It didn't make sense, and yet the weeks passing by didn't seem to dull the pain.

'You're bottling it up,' Suzanne told her, her own eyes cloudy with concern. 'You need to talk it out, not bury it and hope it will go away by itself.'

'What's there to talk about?' Melanie responded, grateful for Suzanne's concern and unspoken support. 'We hardly knew each other. If we'd been courting or engaged I could have understood it, but one lunch is hardly the first step on the way to the altar.'

'And does that really matter?' Suzanne asked. 'You could know a man for years and still not be sure. It only takes a moment, Melanie, a fraction of a second when the world goes crazy and then everything has changed. It can happen in an instant. Believe me, I know.'

'You and Tony?' Melanie asked, suddenly diverted. 'How *did* you two meet? I never did find out.'

'Is this your way of changing the subject?' Suzanne laughed. 'Because if it is, miss, you're wasting your time. You're the one who needs to talk, not me.'

'But you will tell, won't you, Suzanne?' Melanie entreated. 'I'd really like to know. Love at first sight?'

'I suppose you'd call it that,' Suzanne agreed. 'We eloped.'

'How romantic,' Melanie exclaimed, her own smile widening. 'Any particular reason?'

'Well, yes, I guess you could call an irate fiancé and sixty-five wedding guests a pretty solid reason.'

'You eloped on your wedding-day? With another man? You're kidding!' Melanie exclaimed. 'Aren't you?' she added, and, 'Good heavens, Suzanne, I always thought you were the sensible one!'

'Never judge a book by its cover, my dear,' Suzanne chided lightly. 'Now do you see what I'm driving at?'

Melanie nodded. 'It's still a bit hazy, but I think I'm getting the picture. What happened? It must have been something monumental for you to leave a man standing at the altar.'

Suzanne shrugged. 'Tony happened. He was Simon's best man. We didn't meet till the week of the wedding and I knew almost immediately that I couldn't go through with it. But everything was ordered—the cake, the dress, the flowers. Everything was booked and planned—the church, the reception, the honeymoon. The presents were piled high and the ancient aunts and uncles were beginning to crawl out of the woodwork. I couldn't go through with it and yet I couldn't *not* go through with it, if you see what I mean. It was like a fairground carousel, spinning faster and faster, and, the more I wanted it to stop, the faster it went, trapping me.'

'So?'

'So I did nothing. I got up on the morning of the wedding, had my hair done, made up my face, and just waited. Something would happen, something had to happen. When Tony pulled up in a taxi an hour before the wedding I thought he'd come to tell me Simon had changed his mind. I was so relieved, till he took me in his arms, kissed me, told me the real reason he was there. And I didn't say no. I didn't stop to think. We left, just like that, without a backward glance or a single thought for all the chaos we'd be causing, or the heartbreak or the tears. And I've never for a moment regretted it. We didn't know each other either, Melanie, but we took a chance. Perhaps we were lucky, but, there again, perhaps we were just meant to be.'

'And the moral of the story?' Melanie queried with a smile.

'It's very simple, Melanie. If Chase feels as you do he'll be back, you mark my words.'

'Perhaps,' Melanie agreed, eyes misting over. 'But I don't think so, Suzanne. I think I've blown it. He's a proud man and I don't think he's likely to forgive or forget in a hurry. And don't forget, too, I've still got something he wants. If he walked in here tomorrow I wouldn't risk tuppence on my being the reason.'

'Whereas I'd be willing to gamble the crown jewels if I owned them, and I wouldn't lose, Melanie, you just wait and see.'

A couple of days later Melanie was too busy to give much thought to Suzanne's predictions. Tuesday morning's post brought a job interview, one of the many Melanie had optimistically applied for and which, as the weeks had passed, she'd almost given up on.

She set off at the appointed time, a jaunty spring in her step as she parked the Mini and made her way to the modern town centre complex of Turner-Bainbridge. An hour and a half later she met Suzanne for lunch, a tiny smile of satisfaction lighting up her face.

'No need to ask how you got on,' Suzanne greeted her, her own smile widening in pleasure. 'You look like the cat that got the cream.'

'Not quite,' Melanie demurred. 'But I suppose the top of the milk is a start.'

She quickly filled her in on the details. Turner-Bainbridge was an agency, supplying typists and secretaries and other office personnel to a number of towns in the area, Liverpool, Preston, Manchester occasionally but more usually the smaller market towns of the Lancashire plain.

'It's not exactly what I'd hoped for,' Melanie confided over an excellent chicken casserole. 'But it is a beginning, and, given that I haven't actually done office work for over six years, I suppose I should be thankful.'

'So when do you start?' Suzanne enquired, topping up Melanie's wine glass.

'Would you believe tomorrow?' Melanie teasingly asked, laughing outright at Suzanne's start of surprise. She'd spend a week on training, she explained. Her typing speeds were fine, as was her shorthand, but office equipment had undergone a technological revolution in the time Melanie had been away from it. She'd need to be familiar with a whole host of machinery and gadgets she'd only barely heard of.

'After that, well, I go wherever they send me. If I'm lucky I'll be covering for short-term absence—illness or maternity leave for instance. If not, it will be a couple of days here, a couple of days there, Timbucktu today, John O'Groats tomorrow. Naturally I'd prefer something a little more settled, but at least it's a start and the money's a lot better than I'd expected.'

'And, once you've got some experience behind you, you'll be able to look around, find the sort of job you really want.'

Melanie looked thoughtful. 'Yes, I will, won't I?' she mused, and then she raised her glass. 'To the future,' she toasted, 'and whatever it brings.'

It was a lot harder work than she'd expected, Melanie practically falling into bed each evening barely an hour later than Ben, and her waking hours were so full of new experiences that her brain positively teemed with buzz words and electronic jargon. Thoughts of Chase were

pushed well into the background, but, however hard she
tried, Melanie couldn't quite banish them, his deep,
velvety eyes, corners crinkled in amusement, popping
into her mind when she least expected it, echoes of the
shockingly tender moments of their last afternoon
together disconcertingly triggering reactions in a body
she'd hoped was now firmly under control.

The training course behind her, the challenge of a
brand new job helped mask Melanie's nerves as she set
off for her first day's work. Being new, she was to report
direct to the agency at eight a.m. but would receive future
instructions by phone.

'Bit of a crisis, I'm afraid,' Cynthia Jarvis, the section
supervisor, greeted her. 'Half our usual girls have gone
down sick, so heaven only knows how we're going to
fulfil our commitments. We were sending you to Preston
but I've done a hasty re-jig.' She scribbled down an address. 'Can you report in there at eight forty-five?' she
asked, passing the slip of paper across. 'It's a new firm
and it won't exactly enhance our reputation if no one at
all turns up. I'll ring through before you arrive, apologise
for Sally's and Rosie's absence, but, if you could hold
the fort for a few days, I'll see what can be done by the
end of the week.' The telephone rang and she sighed
distractedly, turning away before Melanie could question
her further.

Melanie glanced at the address. It wasn't far, a brisk
five-minute walk from the town centre, and she wondered idly what her day would bring, little dreaming that
she'd find herself plunged into the middle of a living
nightmare.

She found it easily, pushing open the frosted glass
door, stepping into the lushly carpeted, obviously brand
spanking new complex and gazing around with curi-

osity. A door opened behind her and Melanie spun round, her smile of greeting dying on her lips.

'Changed your mind about selling?' Chase asked, recovering his composure first. He'd been as surprised as Melanie for an instant, the shock registering on his face, tightening the muscles of the jawline, darkening his eyes.

'No, Chase,' Melanie replied flatly, and then paused, mind racing, an awful thought occurring as they faced each other, the atmosphere charged with suppressed emotion. She shook her head slightly, almost imperceptibly. No, it couldn't be, the whole idea was ludicrous, preposterous, too far-fetched for words. And yet the sickening doubt remained.

Chase raised an eyebrow. 'In that case, I can't imagine why you're here,' he commented, his tone unmistakably accusing. He waited, clearly expecting Melanie to explain her presence, and, when she didn't, merely shrugged his shoulders. 'My secretary's late, I'm afraid,' he said crisply, pointedly checking his watch. He frowned, flicking her a glance of impatience. 'You're welcome to wait,' he went on, nodding at the easy-chairs grouped about a low table. 'But you'll have to excuse me. I've got work to do, which is more than I can say for one or two others in this quaint little backwater.'

Melanie stiffened at the implied criticism of her home town and its inhabitants, but he'd gone before she had a chance to speak, leaving her stranded in the middle of the reception area, the click of the door behind him emphasising her isolation. She closed her eyes for a moment, still not believing, not wanting to believe the evidence of her own eyes, but nothing had changed when she opened them again, and she swallowed hard, forcing back tears, forcing herself to face the unpalatable truth. It was worse than a nightmare. Every instinct, every fibre

of her body, each and every taut nerve screamed at her
to run, to get away, to put some distance between them,
and yet she couldn't, not if she wanted to keep her job.
She could just imagine the reaction back at the agency.
To walk out on her very first morning without a word
of explanation? She'd be laughed at and then she'd be
back to square one: unemployed and unemployable.
Turner-Bainbridge wouldn't want her and neither would
anyone else once word got round, as it would do. No,
whatever else she did, she *had* to stay, *had* to prove
herself, *had* to swallow her pride, even if it choked her.

She drew her tongue across her lips, moistening them
and pushing clammy hands down the soft material of
her suit in an effort to dry them, urged herself forward.

Chase didn't respond to the low rap of her knuckles
and so she cautiously opened the door, putting her head
round.

He was on the phone, clearly hanging on, impatient
fingers tapping out an angry tattoo on the desk.

He looked up briefly, seemed about to speak and then
turned his attention back to the receiver, offhandedly
beckoning Melanie forward. She allowed the door to
click shut behind her and then leaned back on it, drawing
strength from its solid form.

He'd rung the agency, of course, his voice icily cutting
as he made his displeasure known. Melanie couldn't catch
Cynthia Jarvis's replies but the one-sided conversation
told her everything she needed to know. The entire
population of north-west England found itself branded
incompetent, unreliable and work-shy, and no, he wasn't
prepared to make allowances for the flu-like virus currently rampaging through the town. If Turner-Bainbridge
didn't conjure up at least one competent employee in the

next half hour the resultant bad publicity would damage their credibility beyond repair.

Finally the tone changed. 'You've sent *who*?' he asked incredulously, pinning Melanie with his eyes.

He replaced the receiver none too gently and sat back in his chair, hands behind his head, a snicker of wry amusement shadowing his face. Melanie's heart lurched downwards, settling heavily somewhere in the vicinity of her feet as she forced herself to meet the mocking gaze.

'Well, well, well,' he drawled at long last, patently enjoying her discomfort. 'It looks as if we're stuck with one another, for now at least. I suppose I can find something useful for you to do,' he sneered, deliberately disparaging. 'Answering the telephone, making the coffee, opening letters. It's better than nothing, though only just, and in the meantime I'll ring London, have someone qualified sent up by the weekend.'

'I'm surprised you didn't do that in the first place,' Melanie was stung into retorting.

'As I told you once before, Melanie, my developments are aimed at benefiting the local community, not depriving it, and that includes creating jobs wherever possible. Still,' he shrugged, 'at least I tried. A redundant housekeeper wasn't quite what I had in mind, but you'll do, you'll have to.' The telephone rang as he finished speaking and he grinned across at her evilly. 'Consider yourself employed, Miss Sandford,' he proclaimed with derision, moving to the door, adding silkily, 'I'll be right next door if you need me.'

Melanie seethed silently for the rest of the morning. Chase climbed down from his pedestal of unconcealed delight long enough to brief her, to give her enough background information to deal with most of the calls, if not knowledgeably, at least intelligibly and politely,

Melanie only stooping to seek his assistance as a very last resort.

Chase spent his time dictating letters on to tape, and, though Melanie was conscious that she ought to let him know that her abilities went beyond that of receptionist, some devil inside her wouldn't let her. She would tell him, eventually, when she was ready to, though quite when that would be she wasn't really sure.

As the morning progressed she was glad that she'd stayed. Her initial gut reaction to flee, to put some distance between them, to take the coward's way out, would simply have given Chase another reason to despise her, and she suppressed the band of pain around her heart along with other, more wayward emotions. It was a waste of time raking over the past, opening up still-festering wounds, and so she closed her mind to it all, thankful that pride hadn't allowed her to run away.

In any case, beggars couldn't be choosers, and Melanie hardly needed reminding of how much she had been banking on this job.

Chase emerged from his office at twelve. 'I'm going to lunch,' he informed her, dropping a cassette tape in her lap. 'I've two very important letters that must go out today. Do your best, will you?' he entreated sceptically.

Melanie swallowed her ire. She'd show him. She'd do better than her best and then he'd have to eat his words, wouldn't he? she fumed, deriving a lot of satisfaction from the picture that sprang to mind. She'd finished the lot by two o'clock, not just the two he'd indicated, but the other half-dozen as well, the letters neatly stacked on his desk, awaiting his signature. As Chase walked in, Melanie breezed out.

'I'll take an hour,' she told him, reaching for her handbag.

She didn't need an hour, of course, but she dawdled round the shops, determined not to go back before her time was up. She wasn't particularly hungry either but forced down a sandwich and a coffee before retracing her steps, arriving back at the office on the stroke of three.

Chase was waiting for her, as Melanie had expected, his expression grim, and her heart sank. She should have known she couldn't do right for doing wrong. She should have done what he'd instructed, nothing more, nothing less.

'You didn't tell me you could type,' he began as Melanie regained her seat.

'You didn't ask,' she retorted pertly, waiting for the axe to fall.

'You're very good,' he admitted with grudging admiration as Melanie looked on, speechless. He wasn't angry, then, or at least not with her, although he did have every right to be, she realised with dismay. She *should* have told him, and the fact that she hadn't put her in the wrong. Chase turned away before she could explain.

'I'll put through that call to London now,' he said, crossing to his office. 'It does help that you're considerably better than a two-finger typist, but I still need a personal assistant, someone who knows her way round a word-processor, someone up to date with modern technology.'

'Someone who can create a file, Chase?' Melanie silkily addressed his retreating back. 'Someone who can save a file, who can cope with headers and footers and word-wrap? Someone who knows the difference between a daisy wheel and a dot matrix and who understands the intricacies of electronic mail?'

Her words halted him but he didn't turn round, and Melanie went on, sarcasm creeping into her tone. 'Someone from the local community perhaps?' she enquired scathingly. 'With qualifications other than a degree in washing dishes?'

He spun round, his expression tight, and for a fleeting moment Melanie was sure she'd gone too far. He walked back across the space between them, footsteps muffled in the deep pile of the carpet, and a ripple of fear ran through her as he halted at her desk. He placed both hands on the highly polished surface, leaning forward, his face dangerously close.

'All right, Melanie,' he acknowledged without emotion. 'I think I've got the message. The job's yours, but on one condition.'

'Which is?' she asked warily, dropping her gaze but glancing up through the veiled protection of her lashes.

'No more trip-wires. You've made your point, very thoroughly, but taking perverse delight in watching me fall flat on my face is, from this moment on, strictly off the agenda. Next time I misjudge your capabilities, young lady, you are to tell me so—at once. Understood?'

'Yes, boss!' she couldn't resist replying.

The cool brown eyes flashed dangerously for an instant and then he left her.

Alone in her office, Melanie grinned wickedly. He'd controlled it well, but she'd spotted the involuntary quirk of his lips—and it wasn't one of annoyance!

It was a strange couple of weeks, Melanie still somewhat wary of Chase, always conscious of the power of him, of the way he seemed to ooze masculinity, sexuality, but the relationship was strictly business, conversation confined to the usual banal remarks about the weather or the news.

For Melanie the days simply flew, and although she went home exhausted she was conscious of a job well done and a new respect building in Chase's eyes. She worked hard, the flu epidemic showing no signs of abating, leaving her to cope single-handedly with everything Chase threw at her. Uncomplaining, she cut out her lunch-hour, managing to slot in a sandwich and a coffee in a spare five minutes, often working past the five-thirty deadline till Chase himself came through and quietly insisted she take herself off home.

He worked hard too, another eye-opener, and she couldn't help but gain insight into the workings of his mind. Hilary's vividly painted picture of the ruthless businessman began to fray a little around the edges, though Melanie did see enough of the man behind the image to reinforce the impression that Chase wasn't used to dealing in failure.

Her initial shock at finding him back in the area had given way to vague unease. She'd supposed—wrongly, as it had turned out—that she was his object, that Chase had come back with an increased offer, determined to wear down her resistance. A few days' work in close confinement quickly altered that.

Back in England for the first time in eight years, Chase had no intentions of settling in London, he explained one afternoon in an unexpected lull. Head office for the British side of the organisation could be based there, of course, but plans for a national chain were well in hand. The Banister Corporation was expanding, branching out, diversifying, drawing countless other aspects of property dealing and development into the BANCO group. Success was breeding success and he would move where

needed, deciding on a home for himself once the initial
pressing demands of business had been dealt with. And
if that meant settling permanently in the north-west, he
added, well, why not?

Why not, indeed? Melanie echoed, a shiver running
through her. It wasn't a thought to give her peace of
mind.

'Having second thoughts?' Chase enquired a few days
later, having returned from his own hastily snatched
lunch to find Melanie poring over plans for Lynacre.

She flushed guiltily, like a child caught prying, and
straightened her back, forcing herself to meet his eyes.
'If and when I do, Chase, *if* I do,' she stressed with a
defiant tilt to her chin, 'then you'll be the first to know.
But don't raise your hopes.' She removed the paper-
weights from the corners, allowing the sheets to roll up
under their own momentum, and then slotted them back
into their reinforced tube, conscious of Chase at her
elbow, the faint but distinctive fragrance of Bermuda
Spice aftershave reminding her vividly, painfully of their
afternoon out on Parbold Hill.

'Where you're concerned, Melanie, I haven't got any
hopes. Tell me something,' he added, the tone changing
from scathing to enquiring as he perched on the desk,
continuing to unnerve her with his nearness.

'If I can,' Melanie hedged, unconsciously pushing back
her chair in an effort to create some space between them.

'Haven't you learned anything from the past two
weeks, anything at all?'

'Like what?' she asked, instantly on her guard. The
entire situation had been a real education, but she wasn't
about to tell Chase that. Give him the slightest lever to
her thoughts and he'd wheedle the cottage out of her.
Having studied the plans, she could see now why her

cottage—and, more importantly, her land—was so crucial. She had control of the main drive, making vehicle access almost impossible without her express permission. It hadn't struck her before that the bequest of the cottage, its ground and a thirty-metre border of land around it had been Hilary's way of ensuring that Chase would never get clearance for the sort of scheme Hilary was so opposed to. There was a second driveway—Chase himself had used it on that first afternoon—but it linked up with a narrow and winding country lane, little more than a cart-track, and was totally inadequate to cater for a large volume of traffic. And, of course, if Melanie kept the cottage but sold the land, she'd have the equivalent of a busy main road almost running through her living-room.

'Why did you take this job?' Chase asked, ignoring Melanie's query.

Melanie shrugged her shoulders. 'I needed a job, needed the money. There's nothing unusual in that, surely?' she demanded defensively.

'And which did you need most, the job or the money?' he went on, watching her carefully.

Melanie flushed. 'Both,' she told him firmly. 'In case it slipped your mind, Chase, I had a job until recently. Housekeeper, now redundant.'

Chase grinned, not a bit put out. 'You're never going to let me forget that, are you?' he chided. 'But supposing you didn't need to work, had enough money to live comfortably, then what? Would you still choose to waste your life running after other people, fetching and carrying for peanuts, wearing yourself out in order to make ends meet?'

'Money doesn't grow on trees,' Melanie pointed out.
'I'm simply doing what millions of others do every day
of the year.'

'But you don't have to. Don't you see? Work by all
means if that's what you want, but hell, Melanie, you're
wasted here. You've got a good brain and yet you're
stagnating in an office, mouldering away. You deserve
better than that. I *know*. You've proved it over and over
again these past two weeks.'

'So what do you suggest?' Melanie asked, secretly
warming at the praise and yet suspicious of his motives.
He was leading up to something and it didn't require the
IQ of a genius to figure out what.

'Stop feigning innocence, Melanie, it's an insult to
your intelligence. You know very well what the answer
is, although knowing and admitting it are, in your case,
poles apart.'

'Oh, yes, I think I can hazard a guess,' she acknowledged, springing out of her chair, suddenly aware that
their two-week truce was about to come to an end and
not wanting to go back to their original antagonism. Why
couldn't he simply accept her decision, leave her in peace,
go and build his fun palace or whatever it was somewhere else?

She went over to the coffee machine, busying herself
with cups and saucers, cream and sugar, unaware that
Chase, too, had moved, unaware that he had followed
her across the room, unaware that was until his voice at
her shoulder caused her to jump, almost dropping the
sugar bowl, his presence at her side triggering a panic
response as wave after wave of emotion surged through
her body—anticipation, fear, despair, naked desire, most
of all the desire, as she struggled to maintain an outward
show of calmness and control.

It was pure physical reaction, her body remembering what her mind had striven to forget, that this man could arouse her, *had* aroused her, had jolted her out of the emotional limbo where she'd kept herself for such a long time, had opened a door that Melanie was powerless to close again. He'd made her come alive, for his own selfish reasons, had taken her to the dizziest of heights, had forced her to look life in the face again, and Melanie couldn't turn off the tap of emotion, wasn't sure she wanted to. Her body craved his touch as common sense cried out that it was lunacy, sheer lunacy.

Wanting the touch of his fingers on her naked skin, wanting the pressure of his lips against hers, wanting his body part of her body—simply wanting—was madness, the mere thought inviting trouble. The pleasure would be real enough, she knew that, but at what price?

His hands gripped her shoulders, urgent fingers provoking a trembling response, and Melanie went rigid, fighting to control her breathing, reminding herself that she meant nothing to him, that to Chase life was a game, that she, Melanie, was simply an obstacle to be dealt with whichever way was easiest. He wanted her cottage and to get it would stop at nothing. She couldn't be bought or bullied, he realised that but there was another way, hadn't she already shown him another way?

'Don't be such a fool, Melanie,' he whispered in her ear, drawing her back into his body. 'There's more to life than working your fingers to the bone at someone else's beck and call. You could give this up tomorrow and you know you could. Why not say yes, Melanie, take the money on offer, build yourself a new life, a better life?'

Melanie closed her eyes, no longer hearing the words, just that slow, hypnotic voice pouring over her, soothing her fears, stoking her desires. Every word he said was true, she knew that, and in a way she was tempted, sorely tempted. She *had* enjoyed the work, she knew that too, but it was still very much a novelty. She'd coped single-handedly, rising to the challenge, determined as well to prove herself to Chase, and, though she'd gone home exhausted each evening, as the days progressed she'd begun to realise that the routine of the work rarely varied, and that once the initial strangeness of the technology began to wear off she was no longer stretching herself. In short, she could quickly become bored. With the money from the sale she'd no longer be compelled to spend her time struggling to make a living. She could take time off, pamper herself and Ben, think about a new future, a small business of her own perhaps, remembering long-forgotten dreams that had seemed destined to remain simply flights of fancy.

'Say yes, Melanie,' he urged, his lips making contact with her ear, nuzzling gently before moving on to her temples. 'Just say yes. It won't hurt a bit, you'll see.'

He spun her round, very slowly, brown eyes searching her face, seeking an answer. He tilted her chin, one finger fluttering along her jawline, and all the time the words went on, urging, cajoling, compelling. 'Make it easy for yourself,' he crooned. 'Just say yes.'

And then he kissed her, as Melanie had wanted but hardly hoped for, all her fears melting away as his mouth moved against her own, as his hands traced the curve of hip and waist, pulling her into the highly charged confines of his body.

She sighed as they drew apart, a million regrets running through her, suddenly torn between doing what he wanted and doing what she knew was right. For a fraction of a second she hesitated, the see-saw in her mind tipping almost imperceptibly in Chase's favour.

He looked on, watching the emotions chasing across her face, and then he reached out to draw her back into his arms as Melanie caught the controlled, but unmistakable smile of victory. She froze, and then jerked herself away.

'No, Chase,' she told him, choking back the tears, watching with curious detachment as his expression changed from muted triumph to disbelief, then to anger. 'I can't be bought,' she informed him icily. 'And I'll rot in hell before I allow you to persuade me any other way.'

Jack had been betrayed and Chase was cut from the same mould, ruthless and arrogant, a predator, in Chase's place he doubtless would have, too, but somehow she knew he wouldn't have allowed the fear, the hurt, the pain...

CHAPTER FIVE

IT WASN'T the easiest of weeks but Melanie carried on, seemingly indifferent but sending up a prayer of thanks once Friday afternoon arrived and she took a long, final glance around her office.

Permanent staff had been engaged, permanent *local* staff, Chase had taken pains to emphasise, and, though he had asked Melanie to stay on an extra week to help settle the new girls in, she had politely declined. She had other commitments, she'd told him, knowing full well Turner-Bainbridge would be happy to rearrange them. Chase had accepted her refusal with an indifferent shrug of the shoulders that left Melanie strangely hurt. He could have tried to persuade her, couldn't he? she'd perversely asked herself, attacking the keys of the word processor with unnecessary force.

Her next few days were bitty, an odd day here, an odd day there, physically demanding in their way but leaving her mind free to wander, which it did, annoyingly often, back to Chase, recalling his face in surprising detail, remembering light moments shared, reliving erotic episodes she'd far rather forget. He was no different from any other man, she told herself over and over again. Persuasive, manipulative, ruthlessly single-minded. Ben's father, Jack, Chase, each selfish one way or another; making demands, ignoring other people's needs and feelings, riding roughshod to suit themselves. No, she was right to shy away. Much better not to get involved, not to leave herself open to hurt. After all, she'd trusted

Jack and been betrayed, and Chase was much more open about his motives. It wasn't Melanie he wanted, he'd made no secret of that, but his honesty was little consolation.

At a loose end on the next Sunday afternoon Melanie gave way to an impulse and wandered down the lane to the big house. She viewed it with a critical eye as she drew close, putting herself in Chase's position. It was true that it needed money spending on it, a lot of money, but Melanie still wasn't convinced that the house was the white elephant he had dubbed it. It had been a beautiful building in its day, once part of a large estate comprising several farms, but over the years the farms had been sold off until only the house and grounds remained, with Melanie's cottage on the periphery.

The gardens had been neglected, Hilary's lack of capital making it impossible to keep them as she'd wanted, the young boy responsible for their maintenance barely finding time to keep the lawns tidy. The beautiful shrubberies and rose gardens had long since succumbed to choking weeds. But they could be replanted, Melanie was sure they could, and the house restored to its former glory. It only needed money and a willing owner.

She sighed. Chase had plenty of the former, she knew that only too well, but he had his own ideas for the estate and they didn't coincide with Melanie's. The ironic thing was that in other circumstances Melanie might actually have approved his plans. There was a need for more leisure facilities in the area and his ideas were good ones, she'd recognised that at once, amazed at the amount of thought that had gone into the scheme. But Hilary would have hated it and that was what counted.

She paused at the gate, noticing the loose tiles on the roof, the gaps in the brickwork where cement needed replacing, the peeling woodwork on the eaves and window-frames. Money. That was all it needed. And a family to fill it with love and laughter. It galled her to admit it, but Chase was right. It was too big for the average family, wouldn't be a cheap house to run or maintain. Pulling it down was the obvious answer. Too obvious for Melanie.

She inserted her key and pushed open the front door, standing on the threshold and listening to the sounds of the house. She didn't like it standing empty. These days empty houses were an open invitation to any passing burglar, and she never arrived without wondering if she'd find it intact. But all was quiet, just the familiar creakings of the beams echoing on the air.

For weeks after Hilary's death Melanie had gone down every day, the habit of six years suddenly difficult to break. Chase's arrival had altered that. She'd no right to be there any longer and didn't want to add trespass to her sins. And, since she'd started working, there just hadn't been the time.

Tears filled her eyes as she gazed round at the familiar objects, subconsciously registering the musty odour of neglect, the layers of dust. She brushed the tears away with the back of her hand, a surge of anger running through her. Damn Chase, she muttered, half under her breath. He might be prepared to let the place go to rack and ruin, but she wasn't.

She opened the windows, letting in some fresh air before arming herself with vacuum cleaner and duster and polish. She had a couple of hours to spare. She'd do what she could do. She slipped easily into her old routine, humming as she moved from room to room. It wasn't a difficult task. Even when Hilary had been alive it hadn't been much of a chore. There was none of the clutter old people often chose to surround themselves with, no dust-gathering ornaments, porcelain shepherds with shepherdesses, no commemorative plates and tarnished silver, no aids to memory. 'I don't need them, lass,' Hilary used to tell her. 'It's all inside my head. It's people who matter and no one can destroy what's inside here. I've a lifetime's thoughts and recollections much more precious than the richest jewels.' And, now Hilary was gone, there was only the dust to keep at bay.

Melanie had almost finished when the doorbell rang. She started, almost dropping the carriage clock she had just rewound. More than a little warily she opened the front door and then smiled in relief when Chase stood there.

'Just passing?' she asked, opening the door wide enough for him to enter.

'Hardly,' he replied, following her into the largest of the lounges. 'Though I did call in at your place on the way. Since the Mini was on the drive, I guessed you wouldn't be far. Arriving here to find the windows open, I realised it must be you.'

'What happened to your keys?' she asked, feeling a little awkward once the initial shock had worn off. 'After all, it is your house now.'

He fished in his pockets and pulled out a set of keys. 'And what would you have done if I had let myself in?' he asked, swinging them backwards and forwards before palming them neatly. 'As it is, you looked ready to do ten rounds with Frank Bruno when you opened the door.'

Melanie laughed. 'I wasn't expecting company,' she explained, 'so I wasn't taking any chances.'

'Sensible lady,' he acknowledged. 'But what I don't understand is what you're doing here.'

'Oh!' Melanie's cheeks flamed. 'I'm sorry. I never thought to ask. I suppose I still think of it as Hilary's house and I just——'

'I can see *what* you're doing,' he interrupted with a smile. 'And I don't mind, Melanie, honestly. What I meant was, why are you doing it? The house is empty. It seems, well, a waste of time.'

'Not to me,' she told him. 'It seemed all wrong just to shut the door and turn my back on it. Why, it was practically my home, and, coming down today to find the dust eating its way through the furniture, I simply had to do something. I suppose you think I'm crazy,' she ended lamely.

He smiled again, shaking his head. 'No crazier than anyone else,' he told her. 'And you might even have done me a favour. Show me round and I'll explain.'

Melanie raised her eyebrows. 'But you've seen the house already, haven't you?'

'Not really. I know I did come in, that disastrous first afternoon when I bit your head off at the gate and you paid me back in kind, but I was too annoyed with myself to be bothered looking round. I didn't stay above five minutes and so I didn't see a great deal. Can you spare another fifteen minutes or were you dashing off somewhere?'

'Oh, I think I can manage to fit you in to my very busy schedule,' Melanie teased, relaxing slightly. 'Now, where shall I begin? The pink drawing-room? The blue drawing-room? The orangery? Our guided tours are completely flexible, sir,' she continued in the same light vein. 'Of course, we had to sell the Canalettos—the tax bill, you know—but there's an original Kodak or two on the walls and the draperies are genuine Sanderson. Do step this way.'

They ambled through the house, peering in at the upper rooms, mostly unused and shrouded in dust sheets, but spending more time in the others, Chase idly opening cupboards or drawers as the fancy took him.

It seemed the most natural thing in the world to be there with Chase, answering his questions, satisfying his curiosity, Melanie's residue of nerves vanishing as they slipped into easy conversation. It was as if they understood each other, as if the antagonism and the anger had never been, though Melanie was ever conscious of the effect he continued to have on her wayward emotions.

He was casually dressed, snug-fitting jeans emphasising the slim hips, skimming over the powerful lines of his long, long legs. There wasn't a spare ounce of fat on his body, she decided, remembering clearly the rippling muscles of his torso when they'd come so close to making love. A checked shirt completed the outfit, open at the neck, revealing a dark shadow of hair which Melanie couldn't help but know invited touch, and she blushed, tearing her gaze away, her thoughts far too erotic for her peace of mind. Her recall of detail was, on occasion, much too vivid for comfort.

It was a poignant tour, bringing home to Melanie just how much she missed Hilary, missed her company, her acerbic wit, missed her support. She had never once pried, never asked questions of Melanie, had just accepted her and Ben as part of her life.

Melanie gulped back the tears as they reached Hilary's study. It was the one room in the house she hadn't been in since the funeral. She couldn't. It screamed Hilary, the books on the coffee-table, one open, face down as if relinquished for a moment reluctantly; the stack of

letters in the rack, some of them from Chase, Melanie
supposed; the bag of knitting at the side of the high-
backed chair. The faint aroma of lily of the valley hung
in the air, summoning up an instant picture of Hilary
leaning forward in the chair, glasses perched on the end
of her nose, sharp eyes looking over them, searching for
scissors or tape-measure or a dropped needle.

Melanie blinked and the vision disappeared and it was
Chase who dominated the small and cosy room. She
swallowed the lump which threatened to choke her and
forced herself to move forward, stiffly at first, forced
herself to reach out for the book, turn it over, close it,
replace it on the pile, neatly.

There was a cluster of photographs on the shelf and
Chase picked one up, carrying it to the window. He
looked from the photograph to Melanie and back again.
She was standing in a garden, leaning against a gate,
brightly coloured shrubs around her, a picture-postcard
cottage at her back, the pastel walls and unusual terrace
roof clearly visible. Melanie was smiling into the camera,
not a care in the world, such a contrast to her second
visit to the islands that she felt the pain run through her.

'You've been to Bermuda,' he half asked, half informed her. 'I'd recognise that background in my sleep.
You never mentioned it,' he went on, tohe almost accusing. 'When were you there?'

Melanie told him, giving the more recent date, Ben's
birthday, though Chase wouldn't know that.

He smiled broadly. 'We just missed each other, then.
Six weeks either way and we'd have overlapped. It's a
strange world.'

'Yes, I suppose it is.'

'So what did you think of it?' he asked, obviously
expecting an enthusiastic reply.

Melanie swallowed hard. 'Like the curate's egg,' she told him tonelessly. 'Good in parts.' And then the shutters came down over her face, freezing him out.

She sensed his response, surprise, confusion, hurt, and then he shrugged, leading the way out and down the stairs.

They ended up where they'd started, in the big lounge. Hilary hadn't used this room much unless they had company, but it was Melanie's favourite, spacious and simply decorated, the plain walls of dusky pink the perfect backdrop for the pink and grey fabrics of the upholstery and curtains. It was surprisingly modern, too, the sort of room that featured in the glossy pages of *Perfect Homes* and other up-market publications, with its glass-topped occasional tables, its large, no-nonsense lamps and the low-backed settees grouped around three sides of a square.

'Looking at this, I can see why you're so opposed to my pulling it down,' Chase acknowledged as he followed Melanie across the sumptuous carpets to one of the big windows.

'Does that mean you've changed your mind?' she asked hopefully.

'No, Melanie, I'm afraid it doesn't,' he told her firmly. 'In the middle of summer I'm sure it's everyone's ideal home, but there's a lot of structural work needs doing and the heating system's so hopelessly out of date that it could have come out of the ark. You've done your best, kept it all spotlessly clean and bright, but I didn't miss the signs of mildew in the bathroom, the dried-out patches of winter damp on the bedroom walls. Why on earth Hilary didn't sell it years ago and buy herself a nice little bungalow I'll never know.'

'She didn't want a "nice little bungalow" on a nice little housing estate,' Melanie informed him, catching his inflexion exactly. 'She was happy here, and that's all that was important.'

Chase shrugged. 'That was Hilary's choice. It isn't mine. The house is a bottomless pit. Even in perfect working order it would cost a fortune to run. Harsh though it sounds to you, the house has got to go.'

'And my house, my home?' she queried in a soft voice, her sugary tone belying her rising anger.

'That's up to you,' he told her mildly. 'If you've any sense you'll accept my latest offer, but I don't suppose you will. You've dug your heels in for a fight, so I'm not banking on miracles, not just yet at any rate.'

'But I'll come round, eventually. Is that what you're thinking?'

'That's what I'm hoping,' he replied, moving away.

'And if I don't?' Melanie asked, leaning back against the window, watching his leisurely progress about the room.

He turned, flashing her a sudden smile, the sort of smile that made her legs go weak at the knees, sent a thrill of pleasure running through her.

'Patience, Melanie, like persistence,' he told her, 'is a virtue. I can wait.'

'And what happened to your 'time is money' philosophy?' she jeered. 'Don't tell me you've abandoned plans for another million and decided to join the ranks of the rest of us, make do with second best?'

'I never make do with second best,' he informed her, eyes narrowing dangerously. 'And it doesn't pay to underestimate me either, my dear. You could live to regret it.'

'Threats, Chase? Dear me,' she goaded. 'Hit the ego where it hurt, did I, straight in the pocket?'

'Not at all,' he told her smoothly. 'But if you're hell-bent on doing battle you ought to be prepared for the consequences. Losing isn't a word in my vocabulary and we can't both win, Melanie, not in this instance.'

'You're so certain you're going to win, aren't you?' she demanded. 'You're so self-assured, so damned arrogant that you can't imagine everyone and everything not bowing down before you. Mighty Mr Banister wants, so Mighty Mr Banister gets. Well, not this time, Chase,' she informed him. 'You'll have to think again, once you've recovered from the shock.'

'And who's going to stop me?' he asked. 'You, Melanie?' he derided, the sneering sound reverberating loudly on the air. 'One slip of a girl against the entire Banister organisation? You're deceiving yourself if you think for one moment your intransigence will make a scrap of difference. True enough, I want your cottage and the land, but my plans go ahead with or without your co-operation. I'll find a way, you'll see. And you'll lose, Melanie, in the end. You're losing already, refusing to accept reality, refusing my money. The offer won't remain open indefinitely, and, when I withdraw it, your problems will only just be beginning. You'll be living on a building site, whether you want to or not, and you'll be stuck there, safe and sound in your little house of straw, a house worth next to nothing on the open market.'

'Not to me it isn't. Money isn't the be-all and end-all of my life.'

'No?' he asked coldly. 'I'm beginning to wonder. You're really very good at playing the innocent, too good by half. You could be playing a devious game, Melanie, hoping to make a killing when I fall for your tricks.'

'What tricks? What on earth are you talking about?' Melanie asked, suddenly confused.

'Shall I spell it out?' he exclaimed. 'Tell you exactly what I think? You're holding out. You've convinced yourself that without your cottage my entire scheme will fall flat on its face. You're gambling on my being so desperate to get hold of it that I'll pay any figure you name. This ''it's my home'' plea you keep repeating is merely a screen to cover your hard-as-nails mercenary streak. You've scented easy money and you're going to make damned certain that you get it.'

'Really?' Melanie demanded icily, tossing her head. 'Well, you're entitled to an opinion, Chase, however ill-informed, and you are wrong this time, very wrong. There's only one person here whose life revolves around money and that's you. You're obsessed by it. You've probably enough to take you to the moon and back a dozen times but you're greedy, plain greedy. You'll never have enough. But I have,' she continued, the colour coming and going in her cheeks. 'It might be pin-money to you, but I've a roof over my head, food and drink in my larder, and I don't ask for a great deal else. And as for you, I've had enough of your nasty gibes and your high-handed attitude, blowing hot and cold, flattering me one minute, tearing me apart the next. I've had it up to here, Chase,' she informed him, indicating the top of her head with her hand. 'You can say what you like, think what you like, it won't make a scrap of difference to me. Go ahead and build your pleasure dome, your garden of delight, your whatever it is that you're obsessed with. Drive the M58 right through the middle of my vegetable plot if you can. I'm not budging, not now, not ever.'

She turned and flounced out, not waiting for an answer. She fought the impulse to slam the front door, instead closing it quietly and leaning back against it for a moment, gulping in the sweet fresh air. Her blood was boiling and she covered the half-mile or so to her own house in record time.

So much for her composure, she thought grimly, reaching her garden gate. Why did she let him creep under her skin, stir her emotions? If he wasn't setting her pulse racing with the touch of his fingers he was needling, berating, forcing a reaction. Why couldn't she hang on to her self-control, deny him the satisfaction of watching her rise?

She barely had time to close the front door behind her when the bell went and she knew instinctively that it was Chase. Her first intention was to ignore it—and him, but then some devil inside her forced her to change her mind.

She flung open the front door. 'Good afternoon,' she said, as if talking to a perfect stranger, and, 'Thank you, but no, thanks. Whatever you're selling, I've got one already in pink and another in blue. I know your time must be valuable, so please don't let me detain you.' And she'd closed the door again before he'd even opened his lips.

She went through to the back, filling the kettle, drying the dishes on the draining-board while she waited for it to boil. A sudden rap on the window startled her, causing her to drop a cup, the fragments shattering at her feet.

'What do you want?' she asked, opening the window a fraction. 'Haven't you caused enough chaos for one day, Chase, without pushing your luck?'

'Let me in, Melanie, please,' he entreated.

'Give me one good reason,' she retorted, eyes flinty, not at all impressed by his easy smile.

'I need to ask a favour,' he replied, lips twitching slightly.

'No,' she answered curtly, and promptly shut the window.

'No what?' he mouthed through the glass.

'Just no,' she retorted. 'Whatever you're asking, Chase, it's no, no, no! Now go away and leave me in peace.'

She went through with her drink but he followed her round, standing at the front door, finger permanently glued to the doorbell.

Melanie did her best to ignore the row but eventually he wore her down. 'Well?' she demanded, throwing open the front door.

'Would sorry help?' he asked, attempting to look serious and failing utterly.

'No. It's a very easy word to say but meaningless in your case. Save your breath, Chase, I'm not listening.'

'How about very sorry?' he asked, inserting his foot in the door-jamb, preventing her from shutting him out.

'Not even exceedingly very sorry would induce me to listen any longer. I've had enough, Chase. You've done nothing but insult me since the day we met. No more. I'm beginning to feel like a Yo-Yo, up one day, down the next, and I don't have to put up with it, not from you. Now will you please remove your foot before I slam the door on it and break each and every one of your toes?'

'Be my guest,' he invited, a smile playing about the corners of his mouth.

Melanie's chin shot up at the challenge. 'Don't think I'm not capable of doing just that,' she warned as they faced each other across the doorstep, eyes locked, Melanie's cold and icy, Chase's twinkling with suppressed mirth.

'Five minutes?' he asked, breaking the deadlock. 'And then I'll go away and not bother you again.'

Melanie sighed. 'Five minutes,' she warned. 'And I'm counting every second.'

She moved aside, allowing him to pass, ignoring his smile of triumph. Her ill-temper had disappeared. If she was honest with herself, it had disappeared before she'd arrived home, but she kept up the appearance, deciding it was easier keeping him at arm's length that way.

'Coffee?' he asked hopefully, eyeing her cup as he made himself at home on the settee.

'No, Chase,' she replied, schooling her features into a semblance of severity and taking the chair opposite.

'You're not going to make this easy for me, are you?' he queried, still smiling broadly.

'No, Chase,' she answered simply.

'Not in a very forgiving mood today?' he persisted, not a bit put out by her unbending manner.

'No, Chase.' And, glancing ostentatiously at her watch, 'Four minutes, ten seconds.'

'Is it a game?' he asked. 'Beat the Clock, perhaps? Every Second Counts?'

'No, Chase.'

'No?'

'No!'

'Hm.' He pursed his lips thoughtfully. ' "No, Chase," seems to be the only answer I'm likely to get from the lady, so a change of tactics is called for. Now let me get this straight. I've committed the most unforgivable offence, is that it?'

'No,' Melanie replied, swallowing her smile.

'Progress indeed,' he grinned. 'Now all I need is the right question to trigger the right answer and I've hit the jackpot. After today you never want to set eyes on my again, right?'

'Well——' Melanie stalled.

' "No, Chase," seems as good an answer as any,' he prompted, raising his voice in passable imitation of Melanie.

She smiled, despite herself. 'Very well, then, no, Chase.'

'And if I ask a favour you're going to refuse, aren't you?'

'I might,' she replied, and watched as he shook his head in mock reproval.

'No, no and no were the only answers you were giving with the singular exception of "no, Chase" which has proved the most popular so far.'

'Ah, but that was before I'd wised up to your intentions. And I'm a woman, Chase. Don't forget to take that into account when choosing your next words.'

'And what's that got to do with it?' he asked, leaning forward, allowing his gaze to sweep over her in a manner which suggested he'd never for a moment forgotten she was a female, and a most attractive one at that if his gleam of approval was to be believed.

'Certain prerogatives of the sex—an ability to change our minds as the fancy takes us.'

'Sheer contrary-mindedness, in fact. No, Melanie, to borrow a phrase, I don't believe that, not of you.'

'No, Chase?'

'No.'

Melanie smiled to herself, content to let the silence stretch out between them while she waited for his next attack. Her coffee had gone cold in the cup but she picked it up anyway, swilling it gently round, watching the thin skin that had formed on top buckle and disintegrate.

Opposite, Chase continued to watch her, faint amusement in his eyes as if he never for a moment doubted his ability to wear her down. Melanie met his gaze full on, her eyebrows rising in unconscious challenge, and Chase shifted his position, leaning forward, impatiently pushing away the lock of hair which fell over his eye, giving him a ruffled, almost boyish appearance that tugged at Melanie's heart-strings.

'Why won't you sell?' he asked unexpectedly. 'What's the real reason? I've heard all your excuses but that's just the point, that's all they are—flimsy excuses. The cottage isn't important and you know it. You could live anywhere, you and Ben, an igloo in the frozen wastes, a tent in the middle of a desert. It wouldn't matter where or what it was; if you were there you'd make it home. Why cling to this so stubbornly?'

Melanie's colour rose but she bit her lip, swallowing an angry retort. He was at it again, making judgements, deciding he knew best, claiming to know her mind better than she did herself. And the annoying thing was that he was right, about some things at any rate. Life would be a lot easier with some capital behind her, a cushioning nest-egg. She still remembered vividly the panic that had almost swamped her when Lauren died and Jack walked out. She'd had no one to turn to, no one, her parents having died some years before. She'd needed

money then, security, a roof over her head. She'd been
living in a flat but had had to leave, the tenancy
agreement explicitly excluding children. With the baby
to care for her job had had to go, and without the job
she was penniless, destitute, only the small amount of
money saved towards the wedding keeping her afloat.

Melanie's lips twisted bitterly as the memories flooded
back. How naïve she'd been, expecting Jack's love and
understanding to carry her through it all. How patheti-
cally trusting, and how cruelly she'd been forced to face
the truth. She was on her own. Sink or swim, she was
completely and utterly on her own. Till Hilary had
stepped in and offered her a lifeline. Heaven only knew
what would have happened if Hilary hadn't come along.
She owed her such a lot. Which was why Chase had never
really stood a chance. 'The Banisters,' Hilary had derided
on more than one occasion. 'Money-grabbers. They'd
stop at nothing to make a quick penny. People don't
count, feelings don't count, only money. Uprooting trees
and laying down concrete, that's all they understand.'
No, Chase could make all the plans he wanted but he'd
never turn Lynacre into something Hilary would have
hated. But how to convince Chase of that without revealing too many private thoughts and opinions?

She brought her head up, meeting his gaze squarely.
Swallowing, she took a deep breath. 'Let's just say that
I do have my reasons—complicated, irrational, sentimental or otherwise—and I don't want to sell. Until I
do there's nothing you can do to change my mind. I'll
tell you something else too,' she added, lips tightening
as her thoughts moved on. 'More money won't sway me,
despite what you think.'

Chase smiled ruefully. 'Yes, Melanie, I'm beginning to see that it won't, and in that case I guess I owe you an apology.'

'Another one?' Melanie queried, relaxing again. Two in the space of an hour; honour indeed.

'Another one,' Chase acknowledged, brown eyes beginning to twinkle.

'I don't suppose it will be the last,' Melanie countered acidly.

'No, I don't suppose it will,' he concurred, trying to look penitent, and continued, 'Well?'

'Well what?' she asked, knowing exactly what he meant but not about to make it easy for him.

'Am I forgiven?'

'Again?' she teased. She put her head on one side, feigning serious thought. 'I'm not at all sure that you deserve to be,' she told him mock-severely.

'You're probably right,' he agreed. 'But that's not going to stop you, is it, Melanie?'

'And me being hard as nails? I wouldn't bank on it,' she chided, unable to resist one last dig.

'Ouch! And you a lady too. That one was definitely below the belt.'

'And undeserved?' she asked, lips twitching mischievously.

'Probably not,' he agreed solemnly. 'But "to err is human, to forgive, divine." Here's your chance to prove yourself superior.'

'Who needs proof?' she retorted pertly. 'But you do deserve an answer and you've apologised so nicely. Let me see, how about, "no, Chase"?' she asked, pausing, deliberately provoking.

'"No, Chase"?' he queried, eyes darkening as he watched her.

Melanie's smile spread out across her face. 'To return to your earlier comment,' she informed him, the laughter bubbling up in her throat, 'no, Chase, that isn't going to stop me. Apology accepted—this time!'

CHAPTER SIX

HALF an hour later Ben arrived home, Suzanne giving Melanie a very knowing wink as she turned down an offer of coffee. The film had finished later than she'd expected, she explained, and she was running late. Melanie couldn't help but smile at the gleam of speculation in her friend's green eyes and knew she was in for a ribbing the next time they met.

Ben had loved the film—one of his favourite space adventures—and insisted on showing Chase his own collection of space craft and weapons. Melanie started to protest, sure that Chase must be ready to leave, but he shook his head, a smile on his face, and Melanie swallowed her comment.

She looked on amazed as he joined Ben on the floor, happily taking command of the enemy craft, making just enough 'kills' to lend his defeat credibility.

Ben's face glowed with his success. Melanie was no match for him at all, having a poor grasp of the intricacies of space warfare, and the same game played with Jonathan tended to end in frustration, each child claiming victory, neither prepared to concede defeat, and then retreating into separate corners for a ten-minute sulk till Melanie stepped in with diversions.

'Stay for tea,' she urged Chase impulsively. 'It's only beefburger buns and chips but you'd make a small boy very happy.'

'What about his mum?' Chase asked, lips twitching slightly.

'Oh, I make him happy all the time,' she replied, deliberately misunderstanding. 'Or, at least, I hope I do.'

Chase grinned. 'Round one to you,' he acknowledged admiringly. 'Need a hand?'

Melanie shook her head. 'In my tiny kitchen, even a hand would be in the way. Shan't be long.'

It was a happy meal, Ben chattering on, plying Chase with questions, Melanie adroitly heading off some of his more personal remarks.

'You went away,' Ben began, more of a challenge than a question.

'I'm afraid I did,' Chase replied, equally gravely.

'Mummy said you had work to do. Have you finished it now?' he asked, licking a dollop of tomato ketchup off his fingers.

'Not exactly,' Chase answered. 'I work in lots of places. When I've finished in one I have to start in another.'

'Like Ormskirk?' Ben enquired, succeeding in transferring most of the sauce from fingers to chin and completely unaware of it.

'Yes, like Ormskirk,' Chase agreed.

'Do you live here now?' came the next solemn enquiry.

'Not really,' Chase told him. 'I'll be staying around for a while but when my job's finished I'll be moving on.'

'Where will you go then?' Ben continued, wiping sticky fingers on his napkin.

'Oh, I don't know,' Chase replied. 'I really couldn't say. Back to London maybe,' he explained, his glance flicking across and holding Melanie's for a moment.

'Does your wife live there?' Ben persisted as Melanie flushed with embarrassment.

'Curiosity killed the cat,' she interrupted, and, deciding it was time for a change of subject, sent him into the kitchen for the ice-cream.

'It's all right,' Chase laughed as Ben disappeared. 'Kids are naturally inquisitive. He's doing no harm.'

'Only because you're kind enough not to take offence. He's a bit obsessed with families at the moment. They've been doing a project at school, family trees and ancestors. Ben's just beginning to realise that his doesn't exactly conform to the norm.'

'Leading to some awkward questions, I take it?' Chase observed. 'How do you handle that?'

'I tell him the truth, as far as possible.'

'It doesn't appear to have done him any harm,' Chase commented, stacking the plates.

'The truth, or the circumstances?' Melanie asked.

'Both.' There was a slight pause. 'You must be proud of him. He's a bright kid and much better adjusted than a lot of kids I know whose families do follow the two-parent, two-point-four offspring equation.'

'Thank you. I think so too, but then I'm biased.'

Ben came back with the ice-cream and the conversation turned again.

'Can we go to the park for an hour?' he asked as the meal came to an end. 'Please, Mum, please.'

'What about homework?' Melanie countered. 'You know the rules.'

'Haven't got any,' he replied promptly, raising a laugh in the adults at the patent untruth.

'Scout's honour?' Melanie asked, watching the emotions race across his face as the battle went on in his mind.

'Well, I might have a little bit,' he finally conceded. 'But the story doesn't have to be in till Thursday, honest.'

'And tomorrow?' Melanie persisted.

'Only the photograph for the "guess the baby" competition,' he told her. 'Can I get the albums out and pick one?'

'Of course you can. And then if you're really sure you haven't any homework...?'

Ben shook his head.

'OK, then. Park it is.'

She washed the dishes and tidied up the kitchen, leaving Ben and Chase poring over photographs. She could hear the buzz of conversation, Ben's high trill, Chase's deeper, less hurried responses, and she smiled as she dried her hands.

The two heads were together at the table, the one blond, the shock of hair badly in need of a trim, the other dark, well-groomed, the errant lock falling over his forehead, and Melanie stood and watched them for a moment, heart filling up with emotion. It was so much like the dream she'd had, of Ben growing up just like any normal child, with a mother and a father, a happy family unit; a dream too fragile to endure in the harsh light of day.

'And this is my grandma,' Ben was explaining, pointing to a photograph. 'She used to live in Southport but she went to heaven before I was born. And this is Auntie Suzanne.'

'And who's this?' Chase asked, turning over a page and lifting out the topmost picture.

'Oh, that's Mummy with Auntie Lauren,' Ben supplied, his attention going back to the album.

Chase continued to hold the snapshot. He glanced up, seeing Melanie framed in the doorway, watching him.

'Your sister?' he asked. 'Your twin?'

Melanie swallowed hard. She nodded. 'She died,' she told him, and turned away, blinking back the tears.

'I'm sorry.' He moved quickly, crossing to her side. 'I know the bond between twins is a close one. You must have been devastated.'

'Yes.' She folded her arms, fingers curled around the flesh of her upper arms, hugging herself, fighting for control. It wasn't just Lauren, it was everything—Jack, the shattered dream, Hilary, and Chase himself creating ripples in her life.

Chase hesitated, seemed about to speak, and then placed his hands around her shoulders, squeezing briefly, reassuringly, before going back to Ben, leaving Melanie to pull herself together.

A few minutes later she rejoined them, approving Ben's choice. 'No one's going to guess who that handsome man is,' she declared, rumpling his hair. 'Now run upstairs and fetch my jacket off the bed and we'll be off. I've packed lots of bread, so let's hope the ducks are hungry.' Her eyes met Chase's. 'Thank you,' she murmured.

'For what?' he asked gently.

'For not prying, for understanding.'

'I'm a good listener, too,' he told her, but Melanie shook her head.

'Not yet,' she replied.

Chase smiled, turning her heart over. 'I can wait, Melanie,' he answered intently, the seemingly innocent words sending a shiver of excitement running through her. 'I can wait.'

Suzanne positively gloated. 'Didn't I tell you that you were the magnet? I have a nose for romance, Melanie, an instinct. He's been interested in you all along and this proves it.'

'Really?' Melanie asked, trying hard to suppress the glow that filled her whenever her thoughts turned to Chase. 'Some of us see things in a different light, Suzanne. Some of us keep our heads, Chase Banister included. It's a nice thought but that's all it is, so don't get carried away with any big ideas.'

'Fat chance of that with you pouring cold water on everything I say. But I can wait. Time will tell and then I'll accept your apologies along with the invitation. And don't forget,' she added impishly, 'if you need an extra page boy, Jonathan would look angelic in blue velvet.'

'I'll bear it in mind,' Melanie answered with a smile.

They were sitting in the park while Jonathan and Ben prowled around the lake, fishing nets in hand, optimistically looking for 'tiddlers'. They'd insisted on filling jam jars with water and tying string around the necks, but their efforts at landing the 'big one' had so far proved fruitless and the jars had temporarily passed into the safe-keeping of the two women while the boys continued their dredge for fish.

It was sharp reminder of the last time she'd seen Chase. Ever full of surprises, he'd insisted on joining the expedition to the park. It would give him time to ask that favour, he'd explained, as Melanie had looked startled. It had kept her on edge as they'd strolled around the lake. To anyone looking on it was an everyday scene, the sort of thing repeated the length and breadth of the country as families ended their weekend with an early evening ramble. To Melanie it gave pain, feelings of isolation rising to the surface, battling with other emotions, emotions centred on the man at her side. She was all mixed up inside, not sure how she felt, simply aware that whenever Chase appeared he created havoc in her mind, dominated her thoughts, left her nerves tingling till she didn't know what was worse, Chase present, or Chase absent.

It was almost nine weeks since he'd first walked into her life, turning it upside-down, supremely confident of success, if not one way, then another, and the knowledge that she meant little to him, beyond a pleasant few hours whiled away and his more obvious interest in persuading her to sell, left her more than dissatisfied.

He'd asked his favour and Melanie had acquiesced, swallowing her misgivings. He was likely to be around for several months yet, he'd told her, and, never fond of hotel life, had decided on something a little more settled. He'd had an idea, but, until he'd turned up at Lynacre and Melanie showed him round, that was all it had been. Wandering through the still-elegant rooms, he'd made a decision. The house was empty and habitable, so why not move in? Why not, indeed? Melanie echoed, her pulse beginning to race as she faced up to the reality of Chase living almost on her doorstep. It would probably add to her sleepless nights, but she supposed it was a sensible solution. Chase had it all figured out, would organise a daily to keep the place clean and tidy, rustle up his evening meal, and for one heart-stopping moment Melanie thought he intended asking her. Not that she'd have time now with her agency job, but the thought occurred just the same. Her relief was short-lived. He needed her help, he'd explained. Wardrobes, cupboards, Hilary's belongings needed sorting. He could bring in strangers who'd simply take the lot away, but he was reluctant to do that, feeling it heartless, and would Melanie give him a hand one of the weekends? She'd agreed at once, knowing that it wouldn't be easy, but conscious of his underlying reasons. It was his way of involving Melanie, of making sure she didn't feel left out. She'd been involved with the house for a long time, had known Hilary probably better than anyone else, and as such had a right to be there when Hilary's things were disposed of. Chase seemed to understand that and Melanie was touched. He'd ring, he'd promised, once he'd set a date for moving in, but a week had gone by and the phone had remained noticeably silent.

The boys ran back, Ben's face alight with excitement, but his catch was just an unsuspecting water snail. Disappointed, he agreed to put it back.

'Have you told him yet about Ben?' Suzanne asked when the boys were out of earshot.

'Who?' Melanie asked with assumed innocence.

'The man in the moon, of course, who else?' Suzanne needled. 'So you haven't. Don't you think you should?'

'Oh, sure,' Melanie replied somewhat tartly. 'I've told you before, Suzanne, he's nothing to me, nothing at all. Why on earth should I bore him with my life history?'

'Not yours, Lauren's,' Suzanne persisted. 'It could make all the difference in the world, putting Chase in the picture.'

'You mean in his eyes I'm a fallen woman, someone to pity perhaps, but second-hand, soiled, someone else's cast-off? If that's how he feels then I don't want to know him.'

'You won't get to know him if you don't give yourself a chance. Don't you see, Melanie? You're painting a picture, a distorted picture. Isn't he worth the truth?'

'Maybe,' Melanie agreed. 'And maybe not. Don't forget, I've been through this before. Jack knew the truth and look how he reacted. No, if Chase is interested in me—and I'm still not convinced that he is—then he must take me as he finds me, warts and all. If Ben puts him off then that's Chase's problem.'

'You could regret it.'

'Could I? But then, that's a risk I'm prepared to take. I've learned to stand on my own two feet, Suzanne, I've had to, and I've survived. It might not be your idea of happiness but it's been enough for me. I know you think I'm wrong, avoiding men, avoiding involvements, but it isn't easy learning to trust again, not with my experiences; first Lauren, blithely believing everything Vic Carter told her, and then Jack, refusing to understand, letting me down, hurting me. Who's to say Chase is any different? No,' she shook her head emphatically, 'I'd rather not risk it.'

'OK. I can see your point, but that doesn't mean you have to go to the other extreme. You're not giving yourself a chance, Melanie. You're not living your life, you're enduring it. So what if Jack did walk out on you and Ben? He'd have let you down eventually. Just be thankful it was before you married him and not after. Some men are like that, Melanie, but not all, believe me, not all. And as for Lauren, she simply fell for the oldest trick in the book. But she was young, impressionable, and very, very unlucky. You're not likely to follow in her footsteps; you're much too level-headed.'

'Am I?' Melanie laughed, a harsh, grating sound, full of bitterness. She jumped up, suddenly conscious that the boys were out of sight, and took a couple of steps forward, scanning the periphery of the lake. Suzanne joined her, pointing to the huddle of figures where the stream entered the lake. Recognising the two blond heads, Melanie relaxed slightly. Glancing at Suzanne, she took a deep breath.

'It's only a moment of madness, Suzanne. Who's to say it couldn't happen to me? And yes, I know there are ways and means of making sure that the Bens of this world don't happen. But they do. I know. I almost lost control myself out on the hill and heaven only knows what the outcome might have been. I'm no different from Lauren, not really; a little older, a little wiser, maybe, but still vulnerable, Suzanne, still very vulnerable, and if holding Chase at a distance keeps me safe,' she explained, mentally crossing her fingers, 'then that's what I'll be doing.'

Suzanne sighed. 'Then you're a fool, Melanie Sandford, a fool. But I don't suppose you'll listen to anything I've got to say. Still, before I drop the subject altogether, just let me add—and yes, Melanie, you can ignore me if you want to—but please, whatever else you do, just follow your instincts. It might all go right and it might all go wrong, but at least you won't be looking back on your life in twenty years' time saying "if only". And don't forget, too, you've got something Lauren never had.'

'And what's that?' Melanie asked, recognising the concern behind Suzanne's comments and unexpectedly choked.

'Why, a friend like me, of course. I'll be right behind you all the way.'

'But if I get myself into some of the situations you're hoping for,' Melanie countered, summoning up a smile, 'right behind me is the last place I'd want you to be.'

Chase moved in, Melanie spending an emotion-packed Saturday fulfilling her promise. She hated it. It hurt immensely going through Hilary's possessions, seemed a gross invasion of privacy, but if the job needed doing, and she had to admit that it did, she'd much rather someone who'd known and cared for Hilary scanned the letters, flicked through the photographs, weighed sentiment against common sense before consigning such a lot of it to the rubbish bin.

She'd gone home exhausted, mentally drained, Ben's absence at school camp making it possible to go straight up to bed, but she tossed and turned for most of the night, waking early Sunday morning with a headache. Sunday was a long, long day and Melanie missed Ben's noisy company more than she usually did, and she wondered just how she was going to feel when the main school holidays began and Ben went off to the Lake District with Suzanne and Tony and Jonathan for a fortnight. Still, at least she'd be working. It should keep her from pining too much.

Shaking off her headache, she spent the day catching up on her own chores, the cottage having been somewhat neglected since she'd started her job. By four o'clock, though, she'd finished and was just beginning to feel vaguely dissatisfied when the phone rang.

'Brooding?' Chase asked, not bothering with any preliminaries.

'No. Should I be?' Melanie countered, glad he couldn't see the tell-tale stain of colour in her cheeks which seemed almost a permanent feature of her make-up these days.

'Liar,' he laughed, provoking a similar response at Melanie's end of the line.

'Well, maybe just a teensy-weensy little bit,' she admitted lightly, amazed at his perception. Chase had hidden depths, she was beginning to realise, his understanding two days running immensely touching. With incredible tact he'd left her alone in Hilary's study and bedroom, popping in with regular cups of coffee, occasionally giving her a reassuring squeeze of the shoulders as he removed yet another bag of rubbish. It had been a difficult day and yet Chase had understood just how difficult, finally deciding when Melanie had had enough, forcing her to leave what was left, insisting on pouring her a large brandy before packing her off home. He'd manage the rest, he'd reassured her, and he was very, very grateful.

'I've got a vacant shoulder and a chilled bottle of wine,' Chase now said as Melanie dragged her thoughts back to the present. 'Why not come over later, if you've nothing planned, of course?'

Melanie hesitated, head on one side, once again torn between doing what she wanted and doing what she should in the interests of common sense and safety. Cosy evenings for two over bottles of wine were just the sort of situation she ought to avoid. Even so, she found herself agreeing.

'Does seven-thirty suit?' she asked, deceptively casually.

'Make it eight,' Chase amended. 'I'm expecting a call earlier.'

Melanie walked. It was a pleasant evening and she enjoyed the exercise, the fresh air clearing her mind. Chase opened the door before she could ring the bell, eyebrows rising in surprise as Melanie handed over her own gift-wrapped bottle.

'House-warming present,' she murmured as he removed the wrappings to reveal a bottle of cognac.

'Thank you, Melanie,' he beamed. 'My favourite.'

Melanie warmed under the glow of his approval and followed him into the lounge, the pink room, she noted with pleasure, wondering if Chase felt as she did about it. She accepted the proffered glass of wine and then, out of habit, kicked off her shoes before curling up on one of the settees.

Chase took the one opposite, his long, jeans-clad legs occupying the whole of its length, and Melanie found herself watching, studying him almost, over the rim of her glass.

His hair had grown slightly over the weeks she had known him, softening the angles of his face, giving him a younger, more vulnerable appearance, till the piercing eagle eyes reminded the onlooker that this man would brook no opposition, would not be likely to suffer fools at all. But the gaze that now rested on Melanie showed no hint of this. The eyes were bright, tawny, now thoughtful and gentle, now brimming with humour.

The conversation ebbed and flowed, the silences in between the comfortable silences of friends attuned to the same wavelength. The idea amused her and she smiled to herself. Whatever else was likely, friendship was the last thing she'd expected, especially from a man like Chase—young, rich, good-looking, immensely powerful, exuding sexuality. It was a potent combination, a very appealing combination, as Melanie could testify. She wondered if he thought of Parbold Hill and how he'd come to terms with her rejection. There couldn't be many women who'd said no to Chase and then remained on talking terms, whatever the reason.

Chase drained his glass. 'I'll open another bottle,' he said, standing up, stretching, drawing Melanie's eye up the long, lean lines of his body. He was lucky, having the knack of looking good in whatever he chose to wear. Faded denims or pin-striped suit, he carried his clothes with ease.

'Hungry?' he asked, pausing in the doorway. 'Cheese and biscuits?'

Melanie nodded and then leaned back, cradling her glass in the palm of her hand, happy just to relax and close her eyes.

The phone rang and she jumped visibly, spilling some of her wine. She must have dozed off, more weary than she realised after her restless night. She reached for a tissue as Chase's voice drifted in from the kitchen.

'Answer that, will you, Mel?'

Mel? She bristled for a moment and then tried the diminutive on her tongue, liking the sound of it, she decided as she lifted the receiver.

'Chase, darling,' a voice purred in her ear, a woman's voice.

'This isn't Chase,' Melanie interrupted, her feeling of well-being vanishing at once. She felt the shock waves travel down the phone line.

'Who are you?' the woman demanded, hostility quivering on the air.

'Melanie Sandford,' Melanie replied coolly, and, pointedly, 'Who are *you*?'

'Never mind who *I* am,' the voice at the other end chastised her. 'Just get me Chase.'

'And who shall I say is calling?' Melanie asked, saccharine-sweetly despite the bitter flavour in her mouth.

The woman spluttered but whatever she said next was lost to Melanie.

Chase had appeared in the doorway. Melanie handed over the receiver. 'Some shy young thing,' she murmured with heavy sarcasm. 'Didn't want to leave her name.'

She took herself off to the kitchen, not wanting to be party to one end of the conversation, and finished arranging cheeses on the cheeseboard. She was numb. There had to be a woman in his life—several probably if the truth was known—but she'd closed her mind to it, preferring not to face it, unaware until this moment just how high she'd built her hopes. As she'd told Suzanne, she'd no reason to believe that Chase was even remotely interested in her and yet Melanie had, subconsciously, secretly allowed the idea to form. It was lunacy and she knew it was lunacy, but knowing didn't take away the hurt.

'What on earth did you say to upset Amanda?' Chase asked five minutes later, taking the tray from her and following her back to the lounge.

'Was she upset?' Melanie countered, opening her eyes wide in a mockery of innocence.

Chase's own eyes narrowed. 'You know damn well she was,' he berated, but the mildness of his tone took the sting out of his words.

'In that case,' Melanie told him tightly, 'I can only assume Amanda upset herself. Probably a touch of the green-eyed monsters,' she added, half under her breath.

'Amanda? Jealous? Hm. I wonder why?' he mused, and then flashed her a dazzling smile. 'Pity she didn't have the same effect on you.'

Melanie's cheeks flamed. 'How typical,' she jeered. 'Just like a man, wanting his cake as well as eating it. I must be a real damper to your ego, Chase, refusing to be bowled over by your good looks and your lashings of charm. Quite a novel experience, I'll bet, having to endure the cold shoulder. Tell me,' she added recklessly, the rawness of the pain catching her off guard, allowing her to reveal a lot more than she realised to Chase, standing in the doorway, watching her carefully, unconcealed amusement on his face, 'how do you cope?'

He moved quickly, far too quickly for Melanie to anticipate his actions. He lowered the tray to the coffee-table, closing the distance between them in a few easy strides, and Melanie stumbled backwards as he positioned himself in front of her.

'Are you sure?' he asked huskily, fully aware of the panic rising in her eyes. His generous mouth quirked at the corners, mocking her. 'Quite sure?'

'I...sh—sure?' she stammered, licking parched lips. 'Sure about what?' She clenched her fingers, forcing herself to stand her ground, fighting for control as every instinct, every trembling fibre of her body screamed out for her to bolt, to put distance between them, a lot of distance.

'Your immunity,' he prompted, his voice deepening, thrilling, his breath a warm flutter on her cheeks. 'You wouldn't be afraid of me, would you?' he asked, moving even closer, the gap between them barely maintained. 'And, as you're not afraid, you won't object if I put you to the test, will you, Melanie, will you?'

'I—what?—yes! No!' she ground out, her voice rising with her panic, eyes darting wildly about as she weighed up the chances of escape. He had her caught, almost pinned against the sideboard, and he smiled lazily, sensually, as he reached out, hands gripping her upper arms, pulling her into his body.

The current ran through her like a flame, white-hot, churning, searing.

'Like this,' he purred, mouth against her ear. 'If I hold you close you won't tremble in my arms. If I kiss you like this—and this—and this...' kisses punctuating the words, his lips tracing the outline of her jaw, branding, scorching '...you won't shiver with fear, will you, Melanie, you won't tremble in delight?' His mouth caressed her skin, more feather-light brushes of his lips that turned her knees to jelly, drove away coherent thought.

'If I pull you into my body so you can feel how much I want you, you won't flare up with passion too, will you, my little temptress?' he asked, doing just that, Melanie gasping with the shock, the intimate fusion, his rippling muscles exuding power yet mocking with their taut control. 'Oh, Melanie, you're cold as ice,' he taunted, voice little more than a whisper. 'You're indifferent, impassive, completely immune, and when I kiss you I'll expect you to prove it. Ready now to prove it?' he asked, not waiting for an answer, his lips on her mouth, hungrily, greedily, triggering explosions at the very core of her.

She gave a mew of pleasure deep inside her throat, and his lips relaxed their punishing pressure, now inciting, now exploring, filling Melanie with a glow of happiness, a tide of desire which swept through her, touched each and every part of her, bringing her alive, achingly alive.

His hands slid under her blouse, flesh against flesh, and Melanie urged her body further into his, willing the hands to move upwards, to find her straining breasts, to lift her higher and higher on the waves of pleasure. But though the delicate fingers stroked her smooth skin, erotically traced the curve of her waist, teased the contours of her breasts, they continued to deny her, skirted tantalisingly close to the hard, erect nipples, almost touching, frustrating in their nearness before moving down, pressing into the small of her back, shaping her to him.

A lifetime later he drew away, bright topaz eyes holding hers, seeing to the soul of her. 'Not so indifferent after all,' he murmured, bending his head, brushing her lips lightly with his own. 'Finish your drink,' he ordered hoarsely. 'And then I think I'd better take you home. Heaven only knows what would happen if we put any more theories to the test.'

He drew her down to the settee, fingers fastening around hers for an instant, and Melanie slumped against the cushions, completely drained. She gulped her drink, the ice-cold wine reviving her, bringing her down to earth, though tingling nerve-ends continued to heighten her awareness of the man at her side.

She didn't think, didn't even try to, instinctively aware that she wouldn't be able to think clearly until she was alone, until time had dulled the memory of his branding touch, his plundering mouth.

She followed him out to the car, allowing him to settle her into the passenger seat, sitting passively as he fastened her seatbelt, his hand grazing hers as he pulled away, and Melanie shrank back, scalded, the sharp hiss of in-drawn breath over-loud in the silence.

'Relax, Melanie,' he murmured, taking the wheel. 'I'm not going to eat you. Just relax.'

She barely had time to lean her head back against the cushioned headrest when the car drew up outside the dark windows of the cottage. Melanie jumped up, giving Chase no time to open the passenger door, but if she hoped to shake him off she was in for another disappointment. He followed her up the path, waiting patiently while Melanie fumbled in her bag for her keys.

She inserted the key in the lock, sending up a prayer of thanks as the door swung wide. She turned to Chase, taking a deep breath. 'Thank you,' she told him dismissively, voice not fully under control.

'My pleasure,' he murmured, but he made no attempt to move away and Melanie stood her ground, determined not to allow him across her threshold.

'It was only a kiss, Melanie,' he berated softly. 'Like this.'

And before she had time to fathom his intentions he had stepped forward, slipped his hands around her waist, had kissed her again, briefly, shockingly briefly. He left just as quickly, striding down the path.

'Goodnight, Melanie,' he called out once he'd reached the gate. 'Sweet dreams.'

Some hope.

Late though it was, Melanie recognised that sleep would elude her. She heated up a glass of warm milk, curling up on the settee in her nightie and towelling robe, lights switched off, hugging the darkness to her like a comforting mantle. What had she done? How could she? How could she allow him to catch her unawares, creep under her skin? Hadn't she learned anything at all from that first time? She shivered in the darkness, drawing the robe closer, though the night was a mild one. 'Fool,' she told herself harshly, the single word hanging in the air. She'd known from the start that he was dangerous and yet she'd done it again, almost handing herself to him on a platter, and for what? So that he could take what he wanted—the easy way. He didn't care for her, had never pretended otherwise. He was simply playing games with her, sweetening her up for the kill. All he had to do was bide his time and sooner or later she would fall. Leastways, that was what Chase thought. And why not? She hadn't exactly been the epitome of virginal restraint, had she, reacting so strongly, so wantonly, not once but twice? He was a man of the world and he knew what he was doing, Melanie's heated reactions simply reinforcing it. She was snared and Chase knew it. Like an expert angler he had her caught on a line. Oh, yes, she *seemed* to be free, but that was pure illusion. Try to escape and he'd reel her in, slowly, surely, allowing her to struggle and tire, weakening her, breaking her, till she capitulated, gave him what he wanted, gave away her self-respect.

And the cottage. Mustn't forget the cottage. Melanie, with her transparent emotions and her weak woman's body, was just a means to an end. It was the cottage that he wanted, and she had better never let herself forget it.

She finished the warm milk but sat on, the hours passing by unheeded. Had Lauren ever sat like this, she wondered, dissecting a man's motives, or had Lauren taken the easy words at face value, allowing herself to be used, never suspecting the ultimate rejection once her useful purpose came to an end?

'Fool,' she said again, remembering all too clearly how Lauren's trust had been betrayed, remembering her sister's unshaken conviction that Vic Carter would soon be back to take care of her, her and the baby, refusing to leave Bermuda till he returned. Because Vic had promised. Empty promises, empty words.

For Melanie and Lauren, Bermuda should have been a once-in-a-lifetime experience, a coming-of-age legacy from their parents. They hadn't left a great deal of money but the girls had always agreed that, with college out of the way, they'd treat themselves. A languid month in a near-tropical paradise, a magical interlude before coming back and starting work. Only Lauren had taken one look at the life on offer and decided she was staying. Melanie was horrified, but pleaded in vain. Despite problems over the work permit, Lauren had found herself a job, cabaret singer in one of the big hotels, and nothing Melanie had said could change her mind. And Lauren was happy— for a while—rubbing shoulders with the rich and famous and then, not surprisingly, falling in love, the subsequent news of her pregnancy a bombshell to Melanie.

And still Lauren had refused to come home, stubbornly clinging to her faith in the man she loved. After her death, Melanie had made enquiries. Vic Carter was a playboy, a womaniser. He was thirty-three years old and had just married for the fourth time. While Lauren lay in agony having their child, Vic Carter had been on honeymoon on the opposite side of the world with the eminently more suitable only daughter of an oil magnate. He couldn't even plead ignorance. He'd known Lauren was pregnant when he'd left the islands, his promises to her as lavish as the confetti that would have fluttered through the air at his society wedding, as lavish and as lasting.

And Melanie had returned to England with the baby, heartbroken, disillusioned, and yet still hopeful, turning to Jack, naïvely expecting that he'd help heal the pain, make everything all right again, only to be brought up sharp by his abrupt defection. Two women, two men, two lots of shattered trust. Never again, Melanie had vowed, never again would she let a man get close.

And she hadn't, until Chase Banister came along and dented her armour. His face swam before her eyes, arrogant, angular, cruel, lips curling in derision, and then the image dissolved, reformed, the proud features relaxing, the mouth curving sensuously, the eyes deep, deep pools that she could drown in. Melanie smiled despite herself, remembering the tender moments, and then a voice cut into the picture, shattering the image. Amanda.

The tears took her by surprise, trickling down her cheeks, dropping on to her arms tightly folded across her chest. 'Fool!' she muttered for a third time, brushing them angrily away. 'Why should you care?' And yet she did. Even worse than that—she forced herself to face it at last—she loved him.

CHAPTER SEVEN

MELANIE wouldn't see Chase again, she couldn't. She'd only make even more of a fool of herself and then she'd feel worse than she did already. It explained such a lot, loving him, but how could she have been so blind?

She must have loved him from the start, she realised, beginning to understand why she'd reacted and responded as she had. It was all perfectly natural seen from a new perspective and yet Melanie was still amazed that it had happened. Why hadn't she known? she asked herself over and over. After all, she'd been in love before, should have recognised the symptoms, and yet nothing that had happened with Jack had prepared her for the terrifying mix of emotions that sent her spirits soaring skywards one moment, plunged her into the depths of despair the next. It was a totally new feeling, a contradictory sensation, part of her *wanting* to be in love with Chase, craving the thrill of exquisite pain that pierced her heart at the thought of him, and yet another part, the sensible part, reminding her cruelly how futile any hopes would be. He didn't love her and he never would.

Chase had never lied, never pretended, never feigned affection. He hadn't been interested in her, not particularly, though he'd obviously enjoyed her company, but Melanie didn't kid herself. If it hadn't been for the cottage Chase would never have walked into her life, and, if it weren't for Melanie's refusal to sell, Chase wouldn't have risen to the challenge of forcing her to change her mind.

129

Fate had thrown them together but that didn't mean Melanie couldn't resist the pull, couldn't make every effort to avoid him in future, but she knew, instinctively, that, unless she changed her mind about selling, Chase would always be a threat to her.

She almost found herself wishing that Hilary hadn't left her the cottage. It had seemed a godsend at the time, giving her stability, security, but she had never dreamt how difficult it would make her life. It would be the easiest thing in the world now to acquiesce to Chase's suggestions, to sell up, move out, invest in another house, have money to spare even, and yet she couldn't. Hilary would turn in her grave at the very idea. Hilary had known Lynacre at its peak, had kept the vision firmly fixed in her mind, had never despaired that the estate would be restored in time. She hadn't expected Chase to have the same ideas but she'd made her views known, had hoped he'd think again about demolishing the house, developing the estate, and had deliberately made it difficult for Chase to go ahead with any large-scale commercial venture. Melanie couldn't give in, for Hilary's sake, but how much easier it would make things if she could.

Chase phoned a few days later, Melanie aware, even before she lifted the receiver, that it would be his voice she'd hear. Tempted to take the coward's way out and avoid it, she snatched the receiver up at the last moment, aware that she was only postponing the inevitable. She'd have to talk to him some time and she might just as well do it now.

'Hi,' he drawled, the single word thrilling her, summoning up an instant picture in her mind.

'Hi to you,' she replied carefully, her heart pounding loudly in her ears.

They chatted on for a while, Chase enquiring about Ben—due back tomorrow, thank goodness—and then mentioning work, the weather, the usual inconsequential remarks that characterised small talk, until Melanie's nerves got the better of her.

'What do you want, Chase?' she blurted out baldly.

A low laugh rang in her ears, causing her to smile despite herself. 'Not in a very tactful mood today, Melanie?' he chided. 'Used up your supply of diplomacy?'

'I never had any—remember?' Melanie retorted almost as a challenge.

'Well, yes, now you come to mention it, I do remember, but that was back in the old days, before we got to know each other, surely?'

'Isn't there an expression about leopards never changing their spots?' Melanie pointed out, determined not to weaken, determined to keep the conversation cool.

'Hm! I don't know about leopards, but other, more prickly creatures certainly spring to mind,' he replied, amusement still evident in his tone.

'Well?' Melanie challenged.

'Well, what?'

She closed her eyes for a moment, swallowing a sigh, reminding herself that it wasn't going to be easy but she really must keep him at a distance. She'd tried before and failed, abysmally, but this time she couldn't afford to let him come close.

'Get to the point, Chase,' she prompted as evenly as possible.

He laughed again. 'Something tells me I'll be wasting my breath,' he teased, refusing to be rushed.

'Not to mention time,' Melanie added sharply.

'That too,' he agreed, not a bit put out.

'So?'

'So? You tell me. A hint should do, one of your oh, so gentle, cunningly disguised fists in velvet gloves. Come on, Melanie, spit it out. Tell me what I've done to annoy you now.'

'Guilty conscience?' she couldn't resist needling.

'Not at all, not that I remember, unless, of course, I had one too many the last time we met and ended up too drunk to know what I was doing. Mind you,' he mused thoughtfully, 'I *do* remember the evening in question, very clearly as a matter of fact, and, believe me, it was most enjoyable, most enjoyable indeed. Enlightening, too.'

'And what's that supposed to mean?' Melanie asked, bristling.

'Oh, you know.. informative ... educational ... instructive ... illuminating ... shall I go on?' he enquired, maddeningly blandly.

'Be my guest.' Melanie's voice oozed sarcasm. 'You're obviously dying to share your newly acquired knowledge with someone—but no, on second thoughts, perhaps not. I simply haven't the time to do your pearls of wisdom justice. Some other time, maybe?'

'And what excuse will you be using then?' he asked, suddenly turning serious.

'Not excuses, Chase, just the truth. And if that's another dent to your ego,' she added sweetly, 'I'm sure you'll learn to live with it.' And she hung up before he could reply.

She didn't expect him to ring again, and he didn't, but, ever contrary minded, she found that his silence hurt. She'd begun to get used to his presence in her life, was able to picture him at odd times during the day, aware of his routine and his surroundings, the image in her mind almost tangible. She was acutely conscious, too, that he was living so close, that he probably passed her door three or four times a day and yet didn't take the trouble to call. It was a relief and yet at the same time a torment, and the whole emotional vortex began to affect her concentration. She made some careless mistakes at work, earned herself a reprimand or two, realised that she would have to pull herself together, make a bigger effort not to think of Chase—easier said than done, but at least she could push herself harder, leave no time for idle thoughts.

For once she wasn't looking forward to the weekend. Saturday and Sunday loomed large and empty and she wondered how on earth she would occupy her mind. Ben would help, demanding her assistance at painting or model making, or simply playing games, but there would still be time left over for wayward, unprofitable thoughts.

Dashing out of work on Friday afternoon, collar turned up against the driving rain, Melanie began to suspect that the fates were conspiring to make her life as difficult as possible. The Mini had broken down the day before and was likely to be out of action for another few days. She didn't allow herself to dwell on what the repair bill would be—an arm and a leg probably, but she'd face that when it came. The only stroke of luck was that she was working in Ormskirk. She could so easily have been based in Preston or Manchester and then she really would have had problems.

She reached the bus stop, toying with the idea of walking, hating hanging round in such miserable conditions. A bit of rain wouldn't hurt, she reasoned, scanning the traffic for signs of the familiar red bus. A queue had begun to form behind her, and, assuming that no one would choose to wait long in conditions like these,

Melanie decided that the bus must be due. Five minutes later and thoroughly soaked through, she decided she'd made the wrong decision. Fed up and silently berating herself, she urged herself forward as a car pulled up just in front of her.

'Going my way?' Chase asked through the passenger window.

Melanie hesitated, stunned, the sound of his voice music to her ears. She took a step forward, intending to climb in, and then pulled herself up sharp. Conflicting thoughts ran through her mind—the need to say no, to keep a safe distance; the urge to get out of the rain; the sight she must present, long blonde hair plastered against her skull.

'For pity's sake, Melanie, you look like a drowned rat,' he berated as she continued to hold back. He climbed out of the car, flinging open the passenger door, standing patiently in the cold and wet while Melanie dithered in her mind.

The bus appeared and the queue surged forward, leaving Melanie isolated on the pavement.

'Suit yourself,' Chase muttered, judging his moment to perfection, slamming shut the passenger door as the bus pulled away from the kerb. He strode round to the driver's side with never a backward glance.

'No! Wait!' Melanie shouted, diving forward as he revved the engine. She tugged open the passenger door and tumbled in.

'Don't tell me you finally made up your mind?' he enquired with an evil grin as she fastened her seatbelt.

Melanie flushed but bit her lip, swallowing an acid reply. She was already chilled and miserable without making things worse by scorning a favour.

Chase nudged the car back into the stream of slow-moving traffic and Melanie adjusted her raincoat so that rivulets of water were no longer trickling down her legs.

It should have been a five-minute journey, ten at the most, but the heavens had opened, cutting visibility, reducing traffic to little more than a crawl, and, seeming to underline that there was a celestial cabal, every set of traffic-lights was uncompromisingly red.

'No car?' Chase asked, breaking the uneasy silence.

'No car,' Melanie replied grimly. She outlined the problems, her spirits sinking even lower as Chase put her thoughts into words.

'It might be better to cut your losses and scrap it altogether, buy yourself another. Something three or four years old shouldn't work out too expensive.'

Melanie's colour rose again. No doubt it wouldn't, for someone like Chase, but for Melanie there would have to be a bank loan. Things had improved considerably since she'd been working full-time, but it still wasn't easy making ends meet. Six-year-old boys had the unfortunate tendency to grow upwards and outwards at an alarming rate and she was determined that, whatever else happened, Ben would never suffer. If she could guarantee working in Ormskirk she could do without a car altogether. It would be a minor inconvenience but she'd soon get used to walking or relying on buses, but as long as she was 'temping' that idea was out of the question.

'Of course, you could always spoil yourself, buy a brand-new car,' Chase slipped in with deceptive insouciance.

'Oh, yes?' Melanie snapped, walking straight into the trap. 'And how am I supposed to do that? Money doesn't grow on trees, you know.'

She realised at once what she had done, but by then it was too late to snatch the words back.

Chase grinned, turning his head, pinning her with his gaze. 'It's the logical solution,' he said mildly. 'Why not at least think it over? A new house, a new car—and no thorn in your side.'

'I can live with thorns, thank you,' Melanie retorted huffily. 'And in your case, Chase, you haven't even scratched the surface.'

'So why are you avoiding me?' he asked, quick as a flash.

Melanie squirmed uncomfortably under the steady amber eyes. 'Whatever gave you that idea?' she hedged, praying for the lights to turn to green. Once they were moving she'd be able to avoid the much too perceptive scrutiny, but in the meantime she could only hope to bluff.

'Just a vague impression,' Chase explained, slipping the car into gear. 'A brush-off on the phone, a marked reluctance to share a car with me. Scared I'll talk you round, Melanie, make you see sense? Or is it really me you're shying away from?'

'You?' Melanie laughed nervously. 'Don't be ridiculous.'

Chase shrugged. 'So why the cold shoulder?' he asked, letting out the clutch and inching the car forward.

To Melanie's immense relief they moved off. It was little more than a crawl at first but it was enough to switch his attention to the road, and she relaxed visibly as the car began to gather speed. Thankfully, too, he dropped the subject, though if she knew Chase half as well as she thought she did her reprieve would be short-lived.

It was. He pulled up outside the cottage and switched off the engine, leaping out before Melanie could move. He held open the passenger door and then followed her up the path, waiting while she found her keys. In the circumstances, she had no alternative but to ask him in.

'I'll put the kettle on and change,' she told him curtly, leaving him alone in the lounge. She took her time, stalling, of course, but taking malicious delight as well in keeping him waiting. But if he was aware of her tactics he was hiding it well, instead making the coffee, finding the biscuits, setting the tray and generally making Melanie feel churlish.

'Why are you avoiding me?' he asked again without preamble.

'I'm not avoiding you, Chase. Good grief, you're beginning to sound paranoid.'

'Am I? In that case you won't mind pandering to my insecurities and coming over for dinner at the weekend. And don't panic, you won't be alone. I'll have a houseful of guests by Friday.'

'In that case, one less won't make much difference, will it?'

'Probably not,' he agreed. 'But one more is what I've set my heart on, and you know me, Melanie. Once I've made up my mind...'

Melanie smiled despite herself. 'What happens when you finally meet your match, come up against someone as mulishly determined as you are?' she enquired.

'You mean I haven't already?' he teased, slightly tongue-in-cheek. He leaned forward, the errant lock of hair falling over one eye, and Melanie had an overwhelming urge to reach out, push it back, run her fingers through the soft and silky waves. 'You will come, won't you?' he entreated, his eyes fastened on her face.

'And feel like a fish out of water among your sophisticated friends?' Melanie shook her head.

'What, in that house? Surrounded by things you know, things you've cared for? Now who's being ridiculous?' he derided, raising his eyebrows. 'Say no if that's what you want, but don't hide behind flimsy excuses, Melanie. The place won't be there in another few months. It might be the last chance you get to catch the echoes from the past, see the house full of life, full of people, see it as it was. But don't let me sway you. You're a grown woman, capable of making a rational decision, or at least I think you are. The invitation stands,' he ended abruptly, getting to his feet and marching quickly to the door. 'Seven-thirty Saturday. I'll see you then—maybe.'

Suzanne's Metro had disappeared from sight before Melanie summoned up the courage to climb the worn stone steps. Ben would be happy enough, she knew that, so any qualms about the evening were all for herself. 'Ah, well, here goes,' she murmured, finger on the doorbell.

The door swung open and Chase stood before her, looking stunning in dinner-jacket and white silk dress shirt.

'Forget your key?' he asked, eyes sweeping the length of her, flashing their approval. He didn't seem at all surprised to see her and Melanie was miffed for a moment, almost sorry she hadn't stood firm and stayed at home as she'd intended. She still wasn't sure why she'd come. Almost to the very last moment she'd convinced herself she wouldn't, that nothing on earth would induce her to spend even five minutes in the same room as Chase.

And yet, here she was, accepting the proffered arm without a moment's hesitation, allowing him to lead her into the lounge, introduce her to 'the gang'.

She hadn't realised at the time how angry he'd made her with his pointed remarks and his scathing reactions. It hadn't been until Ben had arrived home half an hour later and she'd found herself snapping over nothing that it had begun to dawn on her that Chase's comments had hit the bull's-eye, and that she wasn't so much annoyed with Chase as with herself for letting him see through her. She *was* avoiding him and he knew it. And he was right about the house, too. It would be in ruins all too soon and it would be nice to recreate a long-lost atmosphere. And at the back of her mind an idea had taken hold. If Chase saw the house at its best, was given a hint of its true potential, it was *just* possible that he might change his mind. It was a long shot, but it wouldn't hurt to hope, would it?

The buzz of conversation halted as six pairs of eyes turned their interested gaze in Melanie's direction. Chase gave her arm a reasssuring squeeze.

'This is Melanie Sandford,' he announced with a smile as Melanie licked her dry lips and tried hard not to look nervous. Chase made the introductions, Melanie nodding at each turn, forcing herself to relax her mouth as she made her shy hellos.

'John and Sheila Macintosh,' Chase was saying. 'Tom Millar, Lucy Sissons, Rob Risewell.' They moved around the room, reaching the second of the two sofas where a young, very beautiful, extremely self-possessed woman glanced up from beneath her lashes. 'And, last, but not least, Amanda Wexford. You two spoke on the phone,' Chase ended as Melanie strove to swallow her disappointment. Somehow she'd expected it but she'd still hoped against hope that the girl whose antagonism had been almost tangible down the phone line wouldn't be one of the party. She heard again the husky 'Chase, darling,' at the same time realising with a shock that Amanda was regarding her with barely concealed hostility.

'Sandford,' Amanda drawled, wrinkling her nose in perplexity. 'Now where have I heard that name before?'

'I don't suppose we're too much of a rare breed,' Melanie responded, making an effort to overcome the other woman's enmity.

Chase handed her a glass of wine, which Melanie drank far too quickly, finding herself seated next to Amanda and spending the next ten minutes fending off a series of questions, each one more personal than the last. By the time she'd started on her second glass Melanie's nervousness had vanished, largely supplanted by annoyance at Amanda's blatant curiosity. Her smile became forced and she glanced wildly round, searching for a way of putting a bit of space between Amanda and herself without being rude, but just then Chase came back in, signalling that dinner was ready and shepherding his guests into the dining-room.

Thankfully Melanie was seated between Tom Millar and Rob Risewell, with Lucy, John and Sheila opposite. Her relief lasted for a whole ten seconds.

Amanda took her place at the foot of the table, facing Chase, the natural position for the host and hostess, and any pleasure Melanie might have derived from the evening seemed about to fly out of the window.

She shouldn't have come, she told herself as the soup plates were being cleared. It was all too apparent what Amanda and Chase had going for them and it wasn't as if Melanie hadn't known. She had, she just hadn't wanted to believe it, hadn't wanted to face up to the inevitable. So what if Chase had kissed her? He'd almost made love to her too, but that hadn't proved anything, other than a healthy male interest in sex.

Pride pulled her through, allowing her to turn with interest to Rob and Tom, discovering that she really liked Chase's friends. They were partners, they told her, not in property development as she'd expected but in their own air courier service, flying lightweight but highly expensive goods around the world at a moment's notice.

'How exciting,' Melanie commented, impressed.

'It has its good points, I suppose,' Tom told her. 'But sometimes I think that they are swamped by the disadvantages.'

Melanie raised her eyebrows in enquiry.

'It makes for rather strained personal relationships,' Rob explained. 'We never really know when we're going to be in England twiddling our thumbs or when we're off on a jaunt somewhere.'

'Yes, I see. A girl in every airport, then?' Melanie teased.

'Some hope,' Rob laughed, turning to Amanda, who was claiming his attention.

Melanie lapsed into silence, pushing the food around on her plate till another voice broke into her troubled thoughts.

'Chase tells me you have a son. How old is he?' It was a soft, faintly Scottish accent.

Melanie smiled across at Sheila Macintosh's friendly features. 'Ben's six,' Melanie told her, and the two women spent a pleasant quarter of an hour swapping stories about the antics of toddlers and the grey hairs they generated in their mothers. Sheila and John had three children, Sheila confided, all boys, and all of them holy terrors.

Melanie laughed. 'I don't know how you cope,' she confessed. 'One's enough to keep me awake at night.'

'You have a child?' Amanda interrupted—rudely in Melanie's estimation.

Melanie nodded, and leaned back warily, waiting for the million-dollar question she knew couldn't be far behind.

'You're divorced, then?' Amanda persisted, watching Melanie carefully.

'No,' Melanie admitted, feeling the *frisson* of surprise run around the room.

'Oh, I see!' Amanda responded, the emphasis clearly on the last two words.

Chase leaned forward, saying something Melanie didn't catch to Sheila, but it served as the cue for conversation to resume, which it did, over-loudly at first, gradually recovering, easing, till they moved back into the lounge for coffee.

Melanie took care to steer clear of Amanda, more than happy to take the seat next to Sheila, enabling them to resume where they had left off, and Melanie kept her eyes away from Chase and Amanda, side by side across the room, refusing to allow her mind to speculate, pushing away unwanted thoughts, unwelcome ideas.

Amanda jumped up eventually, drawing everyone's attention.

'Let's have some music,' she insisted. 'And then we can dance. You don't mind, do you, Chase, darling?' she asked, placing her hand possessively on his arm.

'Chase, darling' merely nodded, leading Amanda to the CD player in the corner and leaving her to choose.

Chase must have brought it with him, Melanie registered subconsciously. Hilary's battered old record player was nowhere to be seen and the thought of Chase beginning to alter the furnishings was immensely reassuring. No one planning on knocking down a house in the very near future bothered with alterations to the décor. But there again, it was probably wishful thinking on her part.

As the lively sounds of a familiar rock 'n' roll number filled the room Melanie slipped out, needing to visit the bathroom. She lingered a while, brushing her hair, touching up her lipstick, studying her reflection in the full-length mirror. She'd been quite proud of her appearance at the start of the night, the one and only evening dress in her possession having been dragged out from the depths of her wardrobe. It was plain and black and dateless, though several years old, hugging the contours of her body before swirling out over her hips into a very full skirt. She'd taken trouble with her make-up too, and decided she could hold her own in any company, any company that was except Amanda's. Sighing, she turned away, making her way downstairs.

Chase came through from the kitchen as she reached the hall.

'I didn't have time to tell you earlier,' he said with a smile as Melanie drew level, 'but you look wonderful, stunning. Black really suits you.'

'Thank you,' Melanie replied, swallowing the lump in her throat at the unexpected compliment. Not that he could mean it. He was being polite, the perfect host, a kind word for everyone. Amanda was the stunning one, her jet-black hair offset by the silver Lurex dress that clung to every curve, highlighting her full breasts, allowing tantalising glimpses of her long, long legs through the fashionably slashed sides of the skirt.

Chase cupped Melanie's elbow, guiding her back into the lounge just as the music changed to a slow, romantic number. 'Come and dance,' he whispered, swinging her round before she could protest, hands on her waist, drawing her close. It was a smoochy number and Melanie's head rested against his shoulder as they shuffled around the area of floor Amanda had given instructions to be cleared. The lights had dimmed too, Melanie noticed, but Chase's body so near, his hands holding her steady, drove other thoughts away, and she closed her eyes, allowing him to guide her, happy, for a few precious moments, to imagine themselves alone and together.

It was a rude awakening, Amanda barely waiting for the music to change before claiming Chase for herself, flashing Melanie a look of triumph as she bore off her prize.

Chase smiled ruefully in Melanie's direction but she chose not to respond, instead accepting gratefully Tom's offer to dance, and then Rob's, and then John's, finally pleading exhaustion and collapsing on the sofa with a glass of wine.

She was glad when coffee was served. It signalled an end to the evening, meant she'd be able to escape to the peace and quiet of the cottage, although being physically away from Chase wouldn't make much difference to her thoughts. Absent or present, he'd still be dominating her mind.

'I'll run you home,' Chase insisted when Melanie rose to leave. She collected her shawl from the hallway, waiting patiently while he dashed upstairs for his keys. She'd feel happier walking. It wouldn't take her long,

though on reflection the long skirt of her dress would
slow her down. It was sheer bad luck that the Mini was
still out of action. As it was several years old, spare parts
weren't easy to come by and it would be Tuesday at the
earliest now before she could pick it up.

There was a sudden surge of noise from the lounge
as someone opened the door, and Melanie spun round,
the idea of accepting another lift home from Chase
making her edgy. To her dismay, Amanda stood there,
dark eyes stormy, a scornful expression on her face.
Melanie's heart sank. Deep down she'd known that she
and Amanda would clash, but even she hadn't expected
it to be quite so soon.

'You're wasting your time,' Amanda snarled, moving
close, threatening. 'Chase could never be interested in
someone like you.' She looked her up and down, contempt oozing from every pore, and Melanie's skin began
to crawl under the ugly blast of her gaze. 'So hands off,'
she rasped, clearly not expecting a response. 'I know
your sort and I know what you're up to, but it won't
work. I won't let it. Chase belongs to me. To *me*, you
understand? And that's the way it's going to stay.'

'Really?' Melanie retorted coolly, resisting the urge to
step back and away from her. 'In that case, you'd better
let Chase know. He seems to have forgotten that he's
spoken for. But then, out of sight is often out of mind,
don't you think? And with someone as virile as Chase...'
She let the sentence hang, her meaning unmistakable,
Amanda's cheeks flaming as the words hit home.

'You're lying,' she spat, obviously intending to say
more but forced to bite back her words as Chase came
into view.

He reached the bottom of the stairs, completely un-aware of the tension hanging in the air, and, taking hold of the shawl, draped it across Melanie's shoulders.

'Ready, Mel?' he asked softly, one hand cupping her elbow.

She nodded, stepping past Amanda, their glances barely meeting, yet locking, the mutual dislike smould-ering, seething.

The moment wasn't long enough to blink and yet their eyes said it all.

You're lying, blasted out the message in Amanda's.

Am I? Melanie's mocked, the ghost of a smile on her lips. Well, if you say so...

CHAPTER EIGHT

A WEEK went by. Melanie immersed herself in work, trying not to let her mind wander up the lane. She saw and heard nothing of Chase and his guests, aware that Amanda and Lucy were staying on past the weekend. John and Sheila were going home to their boys and Tom and Rob were flying out to Melbourne. Amanda was almost—almost but not quite—alone in the house with Chase, and, knowing the layout of the bedrooms so well, Melanie had to make a superhuman effort to steer her thoughts away from them.

Her malicious delight at having needled Amanda hadn't lasted beyond a moment. Following Chase out into the chilly night air, Melanie had sobered at once. What had she done? Who was she kidding? Not Amanda—or not for long, at any rate. Jealousy might have blinded Amanda to the truth but she'd realise soon enough that Melanie was bluffing—and she'd also know why. A woman in love had a sharply honed sense of danger, and how Amanda would gloat when she realised. And if she told Chase what Melanie had hinted at... Melanie shivered. She didn't think it likely, but Amanda was clever enough to exploit it, and Melanie didn't relish the idea of Chase being teasingly informed about her 'crush' on him. Still, it was too late to worry about now, and if they did laugh together at her expense, well, she'd never know, would she?

Instinct told her something else, though. While she and Chase continued to be almost next-door neighbours, Amanda wouldn't be in any hurry to leave Chase alone.

Oh, no! Melanie's heart sank. Not again. Surely there must be some mistake. She scanned again the advance work sheet but it was still there in black and white, the BANCO name almost leaping off the page, and, neatly typed in next to it, her own.

'Sorry, love,' Cynthia Jarvis confirmed five minutes later. 'Mr Banister asked for you by name and he's not the sort of man who brooks any refusal. And since you have worked there before, it does seem only logical.' She shrugged apologetically.

Melanie wandered out, deep in thought, inwardly cursing the impulse to call in at the agency while passing. Normally she waited for Monday morning's phone call, but, since she could be anywhere within a thirty-mile radius, this didn't leave her time to arrive at work by nine o'clock, and, with Ben to sort out for school, it was often a frenetic start to the week. But better another frenzied Monday morning than a spoiled weekend.

Melanie woke with a headache on Monday, her night's sleep anything but restful. She padded to the bathroom, raiding the medicine cupboard for the paracetamol capsules she so rarely needed. Six-thirty. Too early to get up, too late to go back to bed, and yet half an hour with a cold compress might just make a difference.

It didn't. She lay in the darkened room, her thoughts churning, covering the same ground over and over again. By the time she forced herself to get up again, her temples were throbbing and the temptation to ring in sick almost proved too much for her. If she hadn't already known where she was working she would have done, and yet, without the prior knowledge, the headache wouldn't have developed in the first place.

Feeling queasy made her sluggish, and everything that could go wrong did. Ben spilled his glass of milk and Melanie wasted precious minutes mopping up the carpet and finding him a clean set of clothes. Then the Mini refused to start, despite its expensive overhaul, and it took another ten minutes to reach the mechanic on the phone. It was probably the solenoid on the starter motor, he informed her, advising her to tap it with a hammer. If that didn't work he'd call round, but, with a backlog at the garage, he wouldn't be able to make it till lunchtime.

Hammer in hand and gamely resisting the urge to vent her fury on the offending part, Melanie did as instructed. Relief poured over her as the engine spluttered into life, but even that was short-lived. She didn't know how she'd managed it, but there was now an oil stain across the front of her skirt and rubbing at it with a hankie only made things worse. Fighting back tears of frustration, Melanie dashed upstairs. It would have to happen today of all days and it would be her one decent suit.

It was seven minutes past nine exactly when she pushed open the frosted glass door with its distinctive BANCO logo and almost hurtled full-pelt into Chase's arms.

'You're late,' he pointed out coldly before Melanie could catch her breath.

Melanie blenched even further under her pallor. 'Yes, I know,' she acknowledged sickly. 'And I'm very sorry, Chase. It's been one of those mornings and——'

'Skip the excuses,' he interrupted harshly. 'I'm already paying Turner-Bainbridge over the odds for your services, Melanie, and the very least I expect is punctuality. I'll see you in my office in five minutes.'

He turned on his heel and strode out, leaving her stranded in Reception, the tears dangerously close. For two pins she'd walk out, go home, go back to bed, and she sniffed audibly, aware that she couldn't. Apart from her pride in her work, she simply couldn't afford the luxury.

'Don't take it to heart,' a soft voice spoke at her side. 'He's not usually a bear with a sore head, I promise you.'

Melanie turned her head, for the first time really seeing the young receptionist. She'd been vaguely aware that she was there as she'd pushed open the door but Chase had taken her entire attention, his chilly words and arctic manner blocking out everything on the periphery.

Melanie managed a watery smile. 'I have worked here before,' she confided. 'So I know it's out of character. But Chase was right. I *was* late—an unforgivable trait in a secretary.'

'But hardly a capital offence,' the other woman pointed out lightly. She held out her hand. 'Julie Daniels,' she introduced herself. 'And I for one am glad to see you. Coping with this place single-handedly was beginning to look like a distinct possibility, and with the boss in that mood it wasn't the most cheerful of thoughts.'

Being made welcome by one member of staff helped to take the edge off Chase's not so gentle reprimand and the morning wasn't very advanced before Melanie began to understand the cause of Chase's unexpected ill humour, and, since understanding was halfway to forgiving, she soon realised that her untimely—late—arrival was just an unfortunate quirk of fate. Chase was simply letting off steam and she shouldn't take it personally. However, the headache, throbbing away at full throttle by now, had left her touchier than normal and, no matter how hard she rationalised it, she couldn't help but feel depressed.

Chase worked her hard, making sure he was getting value for money, the devil inside her insinuated, and was crisp and businesslike throughout. The past twelve weeks might never have occurred. The root of the problem was another property dealer undercutting BANCO in a multi-million-pound deal. In an effort to attract the right publicity, Chase had already pared his company's estimate to the bone, and anyone offering better terms must either be skimping on materials or carrying a heavy loss. And, since the rival company was headed by his stepfather, Chase made no secret of his views. As far as he was concerned it was an act of sheer spite, and company procedures would need tightening considerably to ensure that future plans remained under wraps until contracts had been exchanged. If work was out to tender, BANCO would have to take its chances, but in other dealings Chase was determined not to be beaten.

'He's great to work for really,' Julie assured her once Chase had gone to lunch and they were able to relax a little. 'Carol, the woman you're covering for, had already booked her holidays when she accepted the job and thought she'd have to cancel. She didn't mind for herself but she hated letting the kids down. But Chase wouldn't hear of it. *And* he insisted on paying her for the week, even though she wasn't entitled. Isn't that amazing?'

Melanie agreed that it was and then swallowed a smile as she resumed her work. She didn't need a crystal ball to tell her that Julie was more than halfway to being in love with Chase herself, despite the diamond solitaire glittering on her finger.

By five-fifteen Melanie had almost finished. Just two more letters, both of which had to catch the post, and then home. She halted, closing her eyes, massaging her temples, easing away the pain. It had been a long day and she sincerely hoped that the rest of the week would follow a different pattern. She half promised herself that if Tuesday began where Monday left off she'd take it as a hint from the powers that be and crawl straight back into bed, but, though the idea was appealing, she knew it was wishful thinking. Chase might have caught her out this morning but it would be the first and last time that he found fault with her work.

Julie took herself off at half-past, Melanie barely glancing up to bid her goodnight, and, engrossed in her task, she didn't hear the other door open ten minutes later.

'What on earth do you think you're doing?' Chase asked, startling her.

Melanie's fingers froze on the keys. For a fleeting moment colour flooded her cheeks and then it drained away, leaving her skin translucent. Smudged blue eyes stared at him, unwittingly vulnerable, unintentionally appealing.

'I was just finishing off,' she explained. 'It shouldn't take me long. And I thought, well, I *was* late, and...' His expression tightened and her voice trailed away.

'Go home, Melanie,' he said wearily. 'You haven't looked well all day. Paying your wages doesn't give me the right to bully you. Go home.'

'Better today?' he asked as Melanie walked in, a calculated fifteen minutes early. His eyes searched her face and then he smiled fleetingly before nodding. 'I've always known you've got guts,' he added unexpectedly. 'So in future, Melanie, don't feel you have to prove it. You don't. Not to me.'

More tears, though this time not the wretched kind. She guessed it was as near as he would get to an apology, and, while not effusive, the words were undeniably sincere.

With Chase's normal good humour restored the atmosphere lightened. Melanie was still kept busy, BANCO's rapidly widening interests generating more and more work, and it was no surprise to Melanie that she was asked to draft a job ad for the local paper not just for one but for two more office personnel.

'Business is booming, then,' Melanie observed during an afternoon break for coffee.

Chase smiled across at her, one of those intimate, heart-stopping moments when the rest of the world ceased to exist for Melanie, and it was with great difficulty that she pulled herself together and paid attention to his words.

'It's an American idea,' he was explaining. 'A whole new approach to holidays and leisure time. Americans don't go off for a week or a fortnight and stay in the same resort. They go on vacation, moving from place to place, staying as long as they like before moving on. We could do that here, given the right incentive. A chain of hotels that are more than hotels with flexible accommodation and eating facilities, extra-special leisure activities, fun pools, children's stewards, beauty salons and so on. All it needs is the magic ingredient—pampered luxury at a down-to-earth price. And I know what you're going to say,' he added, holding up a hand, curtailing her interruption. 'The big hotel groups already have a similar set-up in the major cities, but that's just the point.

Who on earth wants to stay in the middle of a city?' he asked, eyebrows raised in enquiry.

'Businessmen?' Melanie ventured.

'Exactly. Not families on holiday, looking for a base to explore or a place to relax for a few days. Take the kids off their hands and you give parents the freedom to do their own thing. And when they're ready to move on, either because it's planned or on the spur of the moment, they can do so in confidence, knowing that standards are guaranteed. No nasty shocks about the size of the bedrooms or the quality of the food and service. Flexibility, reliability and exceptional value for money.'

'But Britain isn't America,' Melanie protested. 'It's much smaller for a start and doesn't have the kind of weather that encourages people to holiday here. The average British family wants two weeks of sun and sand and sea and is usually prepared to go abroad to find it.'

'Wrong, Melanie,' Chase informed her with a smile. 'That's just one of those long-established myths. There's no such thing as an *average* family for a start. You prove that, you and Ben. And explain away the success of the holiday villages or the popular resorts in Cornwall and Devon. We have a thriving tourist industry in this country already but there's room for a lot more initiative. There's a gap in the market all right, and once the idea catches on, it will snowball, I'm sure of it.'

'All the way to the next million,' Melanie observed wryly.

A single eyebrow rose. 'And why not?' he asked, the light leaving his eyes.

Melanie shrugged. 'No reason, I suppose,' she replied carefully, aware of the definite chill in the air as the atmosphere shifted.

'Ah, yes. I'd forgotten. All those preconceived ideas you have of big, bad Chase exploiting the unsuspecting man in the street. I wonder what it takes to convince you that you're wrong, that yes, I am a businessman determined to make a living—but a decent living, giving value, breeding success on that value and making an honest profit, not stealing other people's hard-earned cash.'

Melanie flushed, tearing her gaze away, unable to deny the truth of what he was saying. She wanted to believe in him, wanted to take his words at face value, but there were too many things stacked against him. He didn't know that her views were based on something more than simple intuition. He knew so little about her after all. And, though a couple of months in Bermuda might not qualify her to judge the world of wheeling and dealing, it was enough to give her an insight into another world, one where money was a god, where acquiring as much as possible as easily as possible was the driving force, and where never a second thought was given to anyone trampled on on the way. And adding flesh to the bones of her opinion was Lauren, her postcards and phone calls for eight months full of everyday life in the millionaires' playground.

'Maybe,' Melanie acknowledged at length. 'And maybe you're right. But you forget, Chase, I know why you're doing this, driving yourself hard. You're plotting your revenge, determined to prove yourself more successful than your stepfather. Well, fair enough, I can understand that,' she added, throwing caution to the winds. 'Up to a point at least. But don't you think you're taking it too far, taking it to extremes? It isn't healthy. Can't you see that? It's—it's—it's an obsession,' she ended, aware from the icy silence that she'd overstepped the mark, remembering too much from a supposedly long-forgotten conversation designed to divert her from her own thoughts, not give her insight into his.

'Have you finished?' he asked at long last, his eyes frigid pools, his mouth set in a grim white line.

Melanie nodded, the pain in her heart almost more than she could bear.

'Good. Perhaps we could get back to work, then.'

It was easier said than done, Melanie finding it difficult to concentrate now that they had clashed again, but at least he left her alone, and she ploughed through the report she was working on, checking and correcting the information before printing, then proof-reading the print-out before making the half a dozen copies Chase had requested. She toyed with the idea of taking the file through but it wasn't needed till morning, and, remembering his anger and his frigid gaze, she decided she couldn't face him again. He'd seemed hurt and vulnerable as well as angry, and she couldn't cope with that, not knowing that somehow she'd helped cause it.

Having made up her mind, she shut the computer down, tidied up, and added the file to the four folders Chase had inadvertently left on her desk. Mindful of his dictum about tightening company procedures, she decided to lock them away. It was highly unlikely that any harm would come to them, but better safe than sorry. She scribbled a note of explanation in case Chase came through after she'd gone and wondered where they were and then carried them over to the filing cabinet, inwardly kicking herself when she found it locked. Sometimes she was simply too efficient for her own good, and, of course, the keys were in her handbag on the other side of the room.

She supposed later that a combination of nerves and haste made her clumsy, for the folders, secure in her grasp one moment, had landed on the floor the next, their contents strewn haphazardly across the carpet. Melanie's heart sank as she took in the mess. Five lots of work from five different folders. She'd no choice really, had she? She'd have to read the lot, sort out which had come from which.

Melanie stifled a sigh. She wasn't late and wasn't in a hurry either, apart from having a desire to escape homewards without bumping into Chase again, and so she knelt on the floor, reaching for the nearest loose sheets, gathering them into a neat pile before glancing at the topmost. What she saw stopped her short.

It was a letter, addressed to Chase himself rather than the company, and it was obvious on scanning it that he'd made a large donation—a large *private* donation—to a children's home, and, from the tone of the letter, it wasn't the first such contribution either. She placed it to one side, dealing with each sheet in turn, many of them routine company business, but many others, like the first, letters of thanks, personal letters of thanks for personal donations. Melanie's cheeks burned as she recalled her taunts and jeers about his making his next million, about the compulsion that coloured his outlook, took over his thoughts, provided motivation. And she was wrong, so very wrong. The letter in her hand proved her wrong. The neat pile of papers to her left proved her wrong and wrong again. No one guilty of the accusations she had levelled would choose to give money away in this manner, or for such a length of time. Yet it didn't make sense, it didn't add up, didn't fit in with what Chase had chosen to tell her after their lunch at the canalside. He *was* determined to prove himself, to reach the top, to stand on

the peak and look down with derision on the stepfather
he hated and despised, Melanie would stake her life on
it. So why this? Another fascinating facet, she realised,
shaking her head, still not understanding but aware that
she'd misjudged him again. And she couldn't even tell
him she was sorry, couldn't apologise, not without revealing she'd had access to a file that quite obviously
didn't carry the BANCO logo, and was clearly marked
in Chase's own distinctive hand, 'PERSONAL'.

She felt the tears well up and brushed them hastily
aside. Tears? For Chase? For herself? Melanie didn't
know, but it gave her plenty to think about on the way
home and later, when Ben had gone to bed and troubled
thoughts could no longer be kept at bay. How arrogant
she'd been, arrogant and wrong, making snap judgements and then clinging to them tenaciously, classing all
rich men in the same category as Vic Carter. Chase clearly
didn't fit the mould she'd cast him in but she'd closed
her eyes to that, ignored the facts, because the facts didn't
agree with her long-held views on people with more
money than sense or principles. And though every day
it seemed something else had happened to give her
another viewpoint, to show her a different Chase, a
caring Chase with a social conscience, a tender Chase
with feelings and vulnerabilities, a generous Chase in all
the ways that mattered, Melanie had blithely gone her
own way, refusing to see the evidence, refusing to see
the truth. And Chase's real crime? Driving himself hard,
retaining the compulsion to carve an empire, to succeed
in a cut-throat world, and not merely to succeed but to
be the best, to stand head and shoulders above the rest,
to cast his stepfather's successes into shadow. Ignoring
the last of these, was there really anything wrong with
his ambition?

Subconsciously she realised what she'd done. Needing to blame someone for Lauren's death, she'd blamed not just Vic Carter but all rich and powerful men, automatically assuming that their morals must be on a par with those of a snake. Because Chase knew what he wanted from life, and had the guts to go after it, brushing aside opposition or neatly side-stepping obstacles, Melanie had decided he was just as corrupt and immoral and ruthless as the Vic Carters who took what they wanted, when they wanted, how they wanted, with never a second thought about the lives they trampled on along the way. And she couldn't have been more wrong, could she? Chase had been brought up in a family where money was never short but he'd built his business up himself, the hard way, not relying on anybody else. Success hadn't been handed to him on a plate and yet, despite his ambitions, his money wasn't all channelled into the business. Some of it—and substantial sums too, Melanie had to admit—was used to make life bearable for sick children and for people a lot less fortunate than himself.

And he'd kept it confidential, had let her taunts wash over him, had never done what guilty people often did— had never gone on the defensive. And perhaps, if she'd stopped to think even for a moment, she might have begun to question her rigid and long-held belief that money and corruption automatically went hand in hand.

It was a chastened Melanie who reported in to work for the remainder of the week, the urge to apologise for her past mistakes uppermost in her mind. But she never could now, and that was her punishment, the cross she had to bear. If Chase had wanted her to know in the first place he'd have told her himself, and it was another point in his favour that he never had, not even when Melanie had

been at her most obnoxious, when anger could easily
have driven him to put the record straight.

Chase seemed distant. In fact, he'd been preoccupied
all week, she decided, looking back, her heart sinking
as she worked out the reason. Amanda. Melanie knew
that Amanda was still around, the brand new shiny red
sports car parked outside the house drawing her eye as
she parked the Mini each evening, constant reminder of
the two of them, alone, or practically alone, sharing
meals, sharing thoughts, sharing things Melanie would
much rather not contemplate but which she did, despite
the hurt it caused. Rubbing salt into wounds might be
painful but it was supposed to help with the healing
process, and perhaps it was time she accepted the truth,
got used to the idea that, though Chase had shown an
interest, it hadn't been in Melanie herself, not really, and
that, whatever happened in the future, she'd be facing
it alone.

'Melanie, can you bring those plans through, the ones
for the leisure hotels, and the feasibility study that goes
with them? And Melanie, if you could rustle up some
coffee, I'd be grateful.'

It didn't take long and she slipped in unobtrusively,
Chase flashing her a smile of thanks as she reached the
door. His ideas for the hotel chain were beginning to
attract a lot of interest. The exact locations remained a
well-guarded secret and would do until he'd signed each
and every land deal, but that wasn't proving an obstacle
to the handful of prospective investors currently ranged
around his desk.

Melanie was glad. He deserved the success and perhaps
it would help take away the sting of her refusal to sell.
He hadn't mentioned the cottage for a while now and
she was relieved. It was probably a change of tactics and

would probably be short-lived but it was one less niggle between them for the time being anyway.

Chase's office door opened; a noisy exodus of businessmen, Chase himself accompanying them out. Melanie collected up the empty coffee-cups, stacking them on the tray before turning her attention to the mountain of papers scattered around his office.

'Leave those,' Chase instructed, strolling in. He seemed immensely pleased with himself and she guessed things had gone well. 'Go to lunch, I'll put these away. No...' He paused, eyes dancing merrily as they rested on her face. 'On second thoughts, *we'll* go to lunch. That down-to-earth pub with the quaint name that serves excellent lunches. The Buck something.'

'The Buck i' th' Vine,' Melanie supplied with a smile, her heart skipping a beat as she met and held his gaze. It was simple euphoria on his part, nothing more, but Melanie would need to be made of steel to remain untouched. 'But what about the plans?' she asked, waving a hand at the chaos on his desk.

'Leave them,' Chase insisted. 'They'll come to no harm for an hour or so. Come on, I'm starving.'

'I thought we were having a security drive,' Melanie pointed out, sorely tempted, and yet at the same time clinging to the shreds of common sense.

'You'll go grey,' he teased, reverting to the Chase she knew so well. 'You'll shrivel up and wrinkle. Stop worrying, Melanie. Nothing's going to happen to the plans and, if it does, you can say, "I told you so". Now, are you coming voluntarily or do I have to carry you out?'

'And have Julie wondering if we've both gone mad?' she teased in turn. 'I think I'd better walk.'

It was a long, leisurely lunch, Chase obviously in no hurry to return to work, and since he was paying her wages—as he'd been so quick to point out at the beginning of the week—Melanie decided it was the boss's prerogative to dawdle. The contrast between Monday and Friday couldn't have been greater but, with Chase in this mood, it was much too easy to forget herself, to let her guard down, to let him come close.

'You haven't asked how the meeting went,' Chase observed once they'd eaten.

Melanie controlled her smile. 'I didn't need to,' she told him demurely. 'Success was written all over your face.'

'And the pound signs were lighting up my eyes, I suppose,' he drawled mockingly, just the merest hint of annoyance in his voice.

'Not that I noticed,' Melanie replied lightly, deliberately not rising to the bait. She picked up her glass, tilting back her head, meeting his gaze full on. 'To BANCO's new venture,' she toasted. 'Here's to success.'

Chase's eyebrows disappeared into his hairline. 'Have you been drinking?' he asked incredulously, double-checking the label on her tonic water bottle. 'What on earth do they put in this stuff these days—pure alcohol?'

Melanie shrugged. 'Perhaps working for the company has given me a new perspective,' she explained, inwardly squirming under the flash of his amusement.

'In that case, Melanie, we'd better make it permanent. Yes, why not?' he asked, leaning forward suddenly, pinning her with his eyes. 'There's a vacancy, Melanie, you know there is. The job's yours, if you'll take it.'

There was a long, long pause while Melanie's thoughts went haywire. He couldn't possibly be serious, and, if he was, she couldn't do it. Work for Chase? Every day? Loving him, wanting him, aching for him, sitting on the sidelines while he lived his life, waiting patiently for the crumbs to come her way; the word of praise, the smile of approval, the acknowledgement of a job well done? Oh, no, she could never do that. She'd die inside. Little by little, every day, some part of her would wither away, and she'd be left an empty shell, her whole life a waste. Oh, no. Far better never to see him again than to live such a parody of life.

'I can't, Chase. Even if I wanted to. I'm under contract to Turner-Bainbridge. For a year, remember?'

'That's not a problem and well you know it,' he snorted in derision. 'What's the matter, Melanie? Frightened you'll mellow? Scared you'll see things my way? Worried you'll want to sell the cottage after all?' The brown eyes mocked her, their dancing lights extinguished. He stood up, pointedly ending their lunch-hour, and, with rapidly sinking spirits, Melanie followed.

'It wouldn't work,' she pointed out as they headed for the door. 'We'd disagree, we'd argue, and sooner or later one of us would blow. And, since you're the boss, I'd be the one out looking for another job. It wouldn't work, Chase,' she repeated as they emerged into the sunshine. 'You know it wouldn't!'

'Do I?' He halted at the car, turning to face her, disconcertingly close as his eyes raked her face. 'I think I was right in the first place,' he informed her. 'You *are* afraid, Melanie, you've been frightened all along, afraid of me, afraid of this.'

And before she could begin to realise what was happening he'd pulled her into his arms, his lips finding her mouth, the kiss persuasive, disturbing, plundering, a violent caress igniting afresh the flames in her heart, sending the blood pounding in her ears.

He lifted his head, iron hands continuing to hold her, the anger in his face dissolving as he took pity on her. 'Melanie, Melanie,' he murmured ruefully, a single finger brushing her bruised lips. 'Come on, we'd better be getting back.'

In a matter of minutes he'd parked the car again, cruising smoothly into place beside Melanie's Mini.

Melanie fumbled with the seatbelt, her insides churning, every trembling fibre of her body attuned to the man at her side. Chase leaned across to release the catch and their hands touched briefly, scorchingly, the sudden hiss of indrawn breath not confined to Melanie, and then she was in his arms again, and it was her mouth that was searching for his, her hands tracing the angles of his face, her fingers entwined in the silky strands of his hair, loving it, loving him. Until common sense snaked in, unlooked for, unwanted, but instantly sobering.

'No, Chase,' she murmured, attempting to pull away. 'Please, Chase, no.'

The dreamlike quality of slow motion set in, *déjà vu* adding terror to the moment. He released her straight away, as he had done once before, his expression no less contemptuous, and she followed him in silence, sick to the heart, nausea rising in her throat.

But the worst wasn't over, she realised, reaching her desk and looking up in surprise as Chase's office door swung open before he could reach it. Amanda was framed in the doorway, her face stony, her eyes darting from Chase's closed features to Melanie's confusion, fastening instantly on the give-away evidence of Melanie's smudged lipstick.

Melanie's head came up, meeting the unconcealed hatred full on, but Amanda turned in scorn away from her, her expression changing at once, the sulky mouth now pouting invitingly as she sailed across the space and into Chase's arms.

'Chase, darling,' she murmured, lifting her face.

He seemed to hesitate for the briefest of moments, his eyes meeting Melanie's across Amanda's head, and a lifetime passed as Melanie held her breath, waiting, simply waiting. Until he kissed Amanda. And with the kiss, the casual gesture, Melanie's fragile world was blown apart.

The afternoon was hell. They were already late back and so time should have flown, but, of course, it didn't, every second seeming like an hour. It didn't help that there was little for Melanie to do, the bulk of the week's work already dealt with.

Amanda and Chase had disappeared quickly into his office, a triumphant Amanda emerging half an hour later, halting for a moment in front of Melanie's desk.

'I thought I told you to leave Chase alone,' she hissed, contemptuous eyes sweeping over her, noting every single feature, Melanie was sure; the one decent suit beginning to look lived-in, the crisp cotton chain-store blouse, the inexpensive shoes. Amanda, of course, looked impeccable, the vivid red designer-made jump suit the perfect foil for the cascade of rich dark hair; the chunky gold jewellery at throat and wrist; the strappy handmade shoes. Melanie felt positively dowdy beside her, the homely sparrow totally eclipsed by the exotic bird of paradise.

Amanda's scarlet lips curled in derision. 'He's simply playing with you, my dear,' she told her confidentially. 'Surely you've realised that by now? He's just taking what's on offer, and, in your case, it isn't costing him a penny. Do yourself a favour,' she added, sauntering over to the door with barely a backward gesture, 'find yourself a boyfriend, someone in your own league. Running after Chase will get you nowhere. He's mine, and that's how it's going to stay. But, of course, you know that already, don't you?'

Five twenty-five. Melanie allowed herself to relax a fraction. Another few minutes and then she could go, and she knew without a shadow of a doubt that she would never be coming back. If it cost her the job with Turner-Bainbridge she was never coming back. She couldn't imagine Chase ever asking for her by name, not again, but fate had a habit of arranging things to suit itself, of tossing spanners in the most ordered routines. Only this time Melanie had had enough. She was running away and staying away, and, if that was tantamount to bowing out of life, then at least it was safer. She'd never be happy, not completely, not knowing what she did, but the pain *would* ease. Eventually.

She glanced around for the very last time, checking everything was tidy, everything in its place, and then reached for her handbag, the door from Reception swinging open as she did so. Thinking it was Julie, Melanie turned to say goodbye, a bright smile summoned up from deep inside. But it wasn't Julie, and Melanie's smile froze as she encountered the other woman's gaze.

Amanda's expression was a mixture of triumph and spite, and Melanie knew instinctively that it wasn't Chase she'd come to see.

'I knew I'd heard that name before,' Amanda began, leaning back on the door, completely at ease. 'Sandford's not so common after all. And then there was the face.

Just *vaguely* familiar. Something I couldn't put my finger on. Quite pretty, I suppose, in an insipid sort of way, but not really memorable. I remember now, though. Oh, yes, I remember now.'

'You don't say,' Melanie countered, eyeing Amanda warily.

'Oh, but I do,' Amanda purred, taking a step nearer, her barely suppressed excitement quivering on the air. Evil seemed to emanate from the very pores of her skin, and Melanie fought the urge to move away.

'Bermuda,' Amanda prompted. 'Six or seven years ago. Remember now? Ah, yes, I thought you might,' she trilled as Melanie's chin shot up. 'Got yourself into trouble, didn't you, my dear? Such a old trick, too. Get yourself pregnant and of course the considerate father simply has to marry you, the considerate *rich* father.'

'No!' Melanie rasped, eyes widening in alarm.

'Yes!' Amanda insisted, moving nearer, subtly threatening, eyes glowing with strange lights. 'Yes!' she repeated as Melanie backed away, reaching the desk and being forced to halt, forced to stand and listen. Amanda's face had come nearer and nearer, her heavy perfume catching in Melanie's throat. Poison, Melanie identified, inconsequentially. Poison. Like the words pouring over her, relentlessly, venom in every syllable, naked hate in every sound.

'But it didn't work out as planned, did it?' Amanda hissed. 'Vic left you high and dry; he left you—and why not? After all, he couldn't be sure it *was* his baby, could he? You had quite a reputation, Miss Butter-Wouldn't-Melt-In-Your-Mouth Sandford. And then your belly swelled, confirming what half the island knew already—that you'd happily sell yourself to the highest bidder.'

'No!' Melanie cried again, too stunned to protest further.

'Yes!' Amanda contradicted gleefully. 'Cold-blooded business transactions. Your body in exchange for hard cash. Melanie Sandford, the island tramp. And you haven't changed one bit, have you?'

'Get out of here,' Melanie rasped, beginning to pull herself together.

'You can't order me anywhere,' Amanda countered icily. 'This is Chase's office. I'm not the one who's leaving. You are. But not until I've finished, not until I've had my say. Poor Chase,' she mocked. 'Yet another unsuspecting victim. He doesn't know the half of it, has no idea of your real motives. He doesn't know the truth about the slut he's employing, the slut he's been seeing on the side.'

'No,' Melanie told her. 'You're wrong, you're very wrong.'

'Tell that one to the fairies,' Amanda sneered, and then her expression changed, sending an icy shiver down Melanie's spine.

Amanda was no longer looking at Melanie, was gazing at a point behind her, and Melanie spun round, the blood draining from her cheeks as she realised what had happened.

Chase filled the doorway, their eyes meeting briefly, locking for a fraction of an instant, the mute appeal in Melanie's dissolving into misery as she met with his response.

Cold contempt blasted out from frigid pools, devastatingly damning, extinguishing fully the last flicker of hope in Melanie's heart.

CHAPTER NINE

IT WAS the hardest thing in the world driving up to the Lakes with Suzanne and Tony, spending the weekend, helping to settle them into the tiny holiday cottage, laughing at the kids' antics, joining in with their games, taking long, rambling walks along the lower fells.

And yet, in the circumstances, it was probably the best thing Melanie could have done. It filled the hours, kept her from seeing over and over again the awful scene in the office when her world had come tumbling down about her ears, blocked out Chase's features with their graphic condemnation. And the knowledge that Amanda was wrong—about so many things—didn't help at all.

To Chase, Melanie was tainted, Ben was living proof of it, so why shouldn't everything else Amanda claimed be true as well? If she'd told him the truth about Ben in the beginning, explained abut Lauren, Amanda's accusations could never have been sustained. And yet she hadn't, and now she was paying the price. And for what? Misplaced pride? Misguided arrogance? Clever Melanie Sandford had known best, about so many things—men, money, power, corruption. And, at the end of the day, she knew nothing, nothing at all, except that the man she loved despised her, now judged her every bit as harshly as she had once judged him. And as Melanie had been wrong, so Chase was wrong. But she could never even begin to tell him. Not now. It was much, much too late.

'Something's on your mind,' Suzanne observed once the kids were in bed and Tony had diplomatically made himself scarce down at the local pub. 'Man trouble?'

Melanie nodded, feeling the tears well up, Suzanne's unspoken sympathy almost more than she could bear. They sat in silence for five minutes, Suzanne wisely allowing Melanie to regain control, and then listening carefully while Melanie poured out the gist of the sorry tale.

'You could always try telling Chase the truth,' she ventured once Melanie had finished and had mopped up her tears.

Melanie shook her head. 'I can't. Not now. It's what I should have done at the beginning, what you told me I should do,' she acknowledged bitterly. 'I was wrong, but now it's too late, much too late.'

'It's never too late if you love him, and you do, Melanie, don't you?' Suzanne probed gently.

Melanie nodded again. 'I didn't realise,' she told him bleakly. 'I was attracted, of course, but then who wouldn't be to a man like Chase?' She ran her fingers through her hair in agitation. 'I just didn't realise. Not until recently. And now it's too late.'

'And yet he knows you had a twin. I'm sure he'd understand if you explained the situation, told him about Lauren.'

'And brand my sister a whore?' Melanie queried. 'It didn't happen that way, I'm sure it didn't. But how do I ever begin to prove it? Amanda was wrong, but right as well up to a point. It's easy to see how it looks to an outsider. Lauren was desperate when Vic left her, and she did flit from one man to another for the next couple of months, she told me so herself. But she didn't sell herself, didn't crawl from one bed to another. Vic was the only man Lauren slept with, the only man she wanted, and he let her down. But who'd believe that now?'

'Chase, maybe, if you gave him the chance?'

'And maybe not. In any case, it's purely academic.' Melanie's voice changed, hardened, matched the granite expression in her eyes. 'I won't be telling Chase anything. I won't be seeing him again. Even without the mix-up over Lauren and myself, there's still Amanda to contend with. He's obviously in love with her, and at the end of the day it doesn't really matter that he believes the worst about me. I'm nothing to him, nothing at all.'

'But are you sure?' Suzanne asked softly, troubled green eyes full of unspoken sympathy.

Melanie returned her gaze. 'Yes,' she told her starkly, the knife-blade twisting in her heart, the knowledge almost unendurable. 'I'm sure.'

Work occupied her days but with Ben on holiday with Suzanne and Tony there were far too many hours left unfilled at the dark end of the day. Melanie slept little, not even bothering to climb the stairs some nights, simply sitting in an armchair, blanket tucked round her knees, book in hand, reading, or trying to, dozing off for an hour or so, reading some more. But more often simply sitting, thinking.

It would ease off in time, she hoped, wondering if she would carry forever the image of Chase, framed in the office doorway, the shock on his face almost tangible. But in the meanwhile there was the present to cope with, the sheer hell of existing every second, every minute, every hour, simply knowing how much she loved him and how futile it was, how unfair it all was. Her eyes were red-rimmed, the tears hovering but rarely allowed to fall as Melanie struggled to rise above her misery, and she reached the end of the week exhausted. She caught sight of her face in the bathroom mirror and realised how dreadful she looked. She really must pull herself together. Ben would be home in another twenty-four hours and he was a sensitive child. She couldn't let him see her like this. Everything had to be normal, or as near normal as she could make it in the circumstances.

She began by spring-cleaning the cottage, throwing herself into the task of scrubbing the bedrooms from top to bottom. It wasn't an essential task but it was physically exhausting and perhaps she'd be able to sleep for once when she finally crawled into bed. She had just finished remaking Ben's bed when the doorbell rang, startling her.

The colour came and went in her cheeks as she headed for the stairs, thinking, illogically, that it could be Chase, wanting it so much to be Chase, wanting it so much *not* to be Chase till she didn't know which would be worse, throwing open the front door to a stranger, or throwing it open to the man she loved, the man whose good opinion she had irretrievably forfeited.

Only it was worse than that. Much worse.

'You little bitch,' Chase began as the door swung open on its hinges. He brushed past her, grabbing her by the wrist at the same time, half dragging her into the lounge.

He spun her round, his eyes shooting flames, the white ring round his mouth telling her more eloquently than words that he was angry, very angry. His hand tightened its grip on hers, causing her to wince with the pain.

'You're hurting me,' she half protested, flinching visibly at the hatred pouring out of Chase's eyes.

'Madam, I haven't even started yet,' he snarled, but he released her roughly, the abrupt gesture sending her sprawling back on to the settee, a ripple of fear running through her, paralysing her mind as she caught the expression in his eyes.

Chase laughed, the mirthless sound echoing horribly inside Melanie's head. 'You had to do it, didn't you?' he demanded, towering over her, eyes mercilessly raking her face. 'Your sordid little plan was scuppered by Amanda and so you had to take your revenge, had to hit out at someone, and who better than the intended victim? You couldn't get me one way; you'd make damn certain you'd get me another. What a twisted mind you have,' he spat, eyes boring into her, holding hers, refusing to allow her to tear her gaze away. 'The final act of revenge from the classic woman scorned.' His face darkened and he leaned forward, threatening, menacing, and Melanie's stomach tightened, knots of pain twisting and wrenching at the core of her. 'What made you so sure I'd have married you, Melanie? Do tell,' he almost crooned, face dangerously close, his eyes travelling the length of her, deliberately, insultingly. 'But no, I don't need your explanation. I think I've worked it out for myself. You couldn't afford to get pregnant, not again, could you, Melanie? So it had to be something different, something novel, something calculated to catch my attention.' He dropped his voice, the words every bit as poisonous in a tone little more than a whisper, and Melanie shrank back against the cushions, trying to block off her mind, trying not to listen, trying to shut out the awful condemnation in those bleak brown eyes.

'Oh, yes, I think I've worked it out. And I could almost salute you, so ingenious have you been.' He laughed again, the most chilling sound Melanie had ever

heard, and the pain intensified, scything through her.
'Sexual frustration,' he hissed. 'Little Miss Sweet and
Coy keeps on dangling the bait and then going all prissy
and innocent till I'm driven half crazy with desire. And
you very nearly made it. Yes!' His lips curled in awful
parody of a smile. 'Chase Banister almost falls for that
one, comes within a hair's breadth of falling for your
she-devil charms.'

'No!' Melanie cried, the single word hanging on the
air for a moment and then fading away in a terrible,
screaming silence.

'Oh, but yes!' he snarled, one hand reaching out,
gripping her upper arm, tugging her roughly towards him
till his face was only inches away from hers. 'And you'd
have succeeded too, but for Amanda. God, what a fool
I've been,' he muttered on a lower note, his anger dying
as he loosened his grip, leaving Melanie to fall back
against the cushions.

He turned away, walking over to the window, staring
out, hands thrust into his pockets, shoulders bowed in
weary resignation.

'Why did you do it, Melanie?' he asked without
turning. 'I didn't believe it at first, I couldn't. Not of
you. I trusted you, like a fool I trusted you. Did you
have to betray me? Did you? Did you?' He spun round
then, his gaze flicking over her, head to toe and back
again, full of cold contempt.

Melanie eyed him warily, vaguely aware at the back
of her mind that something was wrong, that his anger
and hatred were rooted in something beyond her understanding. Chase thought she'd betrayed him, manipu-
lated him, but that didn't account for the intensity of
his reactions. After all, he was a man of the world, more

than wise to the tricks of scheming women. Something didn't make sense.

'Tell me what I've done, Chase,' she entreated quietly.

He started visibly, twin spots of colour burning in his cheeks, and he half took a step towards her, checking himself as Melanie's head shot up in fear.

'You *really* don't know, do you?' he asked in amazement. 'You're like a child caught stealing from its mother's purse. It's not the crime that's important but the betrayal. That's what hurts. You've cost me millions, leaking those plans, but I don't care about the money. Not any more. It's not important. Nothing is.'

He glanced around, as if impressing on his mind every last detail of the tiny room, his eyes coming back to Melanie huddled on the settee, knees drawn up under her chin, arms wrapped around them, hugging them, drawing on their warmth.

'No,' he ended bleakly. 'Nothing is.'

The pain was almost more than Melanie could bear. She was devastated, the sick feeling in the pit of her stomach spreading upwards, gripping her as wave after wave of nausea swept over her.

It didn't even help that he was wrong. He believed it, that was enough. She still only half understood what she'd been accused of, too much having happened all at once for Melanie to begin to make sense of it. But the whole thing became clearer the following morning.

She couldn't face breakfast but she'd made herself some tea, half-heartedly thumbing through the *Guardian* while she waited for the kettle to boil. Her mind was numb, the words on the page a meaningless jumble of hieroglyphics till a single word caught her attention, jumped out at her. Her knees gave way and she groped her way to a stool, shaking fingers smoothing out the paper.

'BANCO Plans on Ice,' ran the headline on the inside page, and the words swam before her eyes, the tears hovering on her lashes, distorting and magnifying till Melanie dashed them impatiently away.

She had to read the article three times before she began to make sense of it, but bit by bit the pieces of the puzzle began to give her an idea of what had happened, and, more importantly, of who was to blame.

For the second time in as many months important plans had been leaked to a rival company. Only this time it was the hotel leisure scheme Chase had been pinning his hopes on. As before, the other company had moved quickly, buying up key sites and forcing BANCO to improve considerably its offers for the rest. And there was more.

A BANCO spokesman was unable to confirm that the company would be seeking alternative sites for its developments. But it seems unlikely that the idea will be dropped altogether. On a personal note, Chase Banister, who has built up the multi-million-pound organisation from scratch over the past eight years, is likely to be feeling more than a little aggrieved at this latest setback. The rival company, Penmanning, is owned and run by his stepfather, and the two men are reported to be 'mutually hostile.'

Melanie would never know for certain, but instinct told her that the person with most to gain from leaking those plans and letting Melanie conveniently shoulder the blame was Amanda. And, of course, hadn't Amanda had the golden opportunity?

*   *   *

The bungalow was quiet without the kids but the silence suited Melanie's mood. She was surprised to find herself alone at last, and curled up on the settee, a magazine open on the cushions beside her, the pages idly flicked through, half-heartedly scanned.

All Suzanne's efforts over the past three weeks had seemed bent on ensuring that Melanie was never left alone for a single moment, never given the chance to brood, and so her decision to take the boys to the cinema for the afternoon and give Melanie some peace and quiet was all the more strange.

Melanie thought back over the morning, something troubling her, nothing she could put her finger on but vaguely there in the background. She sighed, closing the magazine, closing her eyes, brushing away the solitary tear that squeezed itself out from underneath lashes and trickled down her cheek. She didn't want to think about him but every waking moment was filled with his image, the sound of his voice, the familiar smiles and gestures; and her nights were torn apart by his anger and contempt, the blazing fury in his eyes, and, worse, the disappointment behind it all.

Melanie had moved quickly once everything became clear, contacting her solicitors immediately with instructions to sell the cottage to Chase for whatever figure he was prepared to offer, and moving out four days later.

She had intended staying at a hotel for a week or two, until she'd found somewhere else for herself and Ben to live. But Suzanne had gently overruled her, insisting that there was plenty of room at the bungalow, and Melanie had been in no fit state to object. Ben could share with Jonathan, and Melanie could have the guest room.

Melanie had spent the time ringing round the estate agents, poring over photographs and descriptions of

houses, occasionally mustering the enthusiasm to actually go and view, but so far nothing had taken her
fancy and Suzanne and Tony had repeated their assur-
ances that she and Ben could stay for as long as they
wanted. They were more than welcome, Suzanne assured her, brushing aside Melanie's thanks, and, after
all, what were friends for, if not to help out in times of
trouble?

The magazine slipped to the floor with a rustle of
papers, the sound over-loud in the silence, but Melanie
ignored it, left it where it was, not interested, instead
reaching for the by now lukewarm cup of tea.

Almost immediately the doorbell rang, startling her,
and some of the tea spilled over into the saucer. Melanie
reached for the box of tissues on the sideboard, dabbing
at her skirt where the drink had spotted, at the same
time crossing to the window and peering out through the
curtains.

A car was parked outside the gates, gleaming silver in
the afternoon sunshine, and Melanie's heart slowed to
a more normal rate as disappointment ran through her,
extinguishing a faint glimmer of hope. Her mouth twisted
into a tight smile as she moved woodenly to the hallway.
What hope? she asked herself. Chase was lost to her
now, his good opinion of her irrevocably shattered.
Melanie was the last person in the world he'd come
looking for, and, besides, nobody knew she was here,
only Suzanne and Tony.

She saw the shadowy outline of a figure through the
frosted glass and brought herself up sharp, imagining,
foolishly, that it *was* Chase, that he really had come to
see her. She swallowed the bitter flavour in her mouth.
Oh, yes, he'd really do that, wouldn't he? Even if the
truth about the plans came out and Melanie was cleared

of all blame, Amanda's accusations hung between them, Melanie's reputation in shreds.

She wiped away a tear with the back of her hand, amazed there were tears left to fall, and, taking a deep breath, opened the front door.

'Hi.' Chase looked strained, the corners of his mouth etched with lines that hadn't been there three weeks earlier, his eyes heavy with suppressed emotion.

Melanie took an involuntary step backwards, closing her eyes for an instant, not believing, hardly daring to believe.

He was still there when she lifted her lids, an unfathomable expression on his face, but the naked anger and contempt that Melanie remembered so clearly from their last meeting had completely disappeared.

'Can I come in?' he asked, his eyes holding hers.

Melanie nodded, swallowing hard, moving back into the lounge where she stood in awkward silence, her fingers nervously clenched together, the colour alternately flooding and draining her face.

'I had to come,' Chase began as Melanie subconsciously registered the uncertainty in his voice. 'There was so much that couldn't be ignored, couldn't be said in a letter or over the phone. Can I sit down?' he asked, gesturing to the sofa behind her.

Melanie nodded again, backing to the cushions, perching herself on the edge, her body half turned to face him as he joined her.

'I was wrong,' he said simply, eyes never leaving her face.

'About what?' she asked, finding her voice at last, painfully aware of his body so close to hers.

'About a lot of things,' came the strange reply as the brooding eyes continued to search her face as if looking

for answers. 'Amanda leaked the plans,' he said quietly.
'I'm sorry, Melanie. I don't know what else to say.'

Melanie closed her eyes again, holding back the
scalding tears. It didn't help, not really. He might not
hate her any more but he'd always despise her; Amanda's
accusations had seen to that. In his mind Melanie was
a slut and she couldn't clear her own name without
blackening Lauren's, something Melanie would never do.
It all seemed so unfair, especially when Lauren's only
crime, like Melanie's, had been to fall in love.

Chase sighed heavily and Melanie's eyes flew open,
sensing his distress.

'I shouldn't have come,' he said. 'I've hurt you enough
without putting you through the ordeal of making polite
conversation. I was going to write, but I—it—well—it
seemed the coward's way out, I suppose.'

'No. I'm glad you came yourself,' Melanie told him
from the bottom of her heart. It would make a difference later, knowing that they'd parted without ani-
mosity, knowing that her nights would no longer be torn
apart by the hatred and anger pouring from his eyes.

'So am I—now,' he admitted, raising the ghost of a
smile. 'I needed to make sure you were all right,' he explained as Melanie's eyebrows rose in enquiry. His voice
changed, the pain tearing at Melanie's heart. 'I said a
lot of despicable things, Melanie.'

'Yes.'

'Too many to forgive? No, that's unfair of me,' he
countered as Melanie's head shot up in surprise.

'I do understand, Chase. You weren't to know,' she
answered softly. 'I was the obvious culprit. I realise that
now.'

'Too obvious. I'd forgotten Amanda's streak of ruth-
lessness. She's rich and beautiful, used to getting her

own way. She saw you as a threat,' he explained, sensing Melanie's confusion.

'Oh!' Her cheeks reddened and she tore her gaze away, staring out of the window. How ridiculous, a woman like Amanda jealous of her, a woman with the world at her feet—good looks, lively personality, more money than Melanie could ever dream of, and, most of all, most importantly, Chase.

'I could have wrung her pretty neck,' he went on. 'I might have done too, if she hadn't gone to ground. She's a lot to answer for, but the damage is done now.'

'Yes.' Melanie wondered, vaguely, what he'd meant by Amanda's going to ground. Surely he'd understand, could find it in his heart to forgive the woman he loved? After all, Amanda had only reacted instinctively, protecting what was hers. It might have hurt Chase financially but he'd recover in time, and Amanda herself was an heiress.

'You've got a new car,' she observed, picking out the silvery outline through the pattern of nets at the window.

'Yes. My consolation prize for losing,' he replied bitterly.

'Was it such a major setback?' she asked, a nervous finger tracing the outline of flowers on a cushion.

'Financially, yes. But that doesn't seem important now. It was—other things that I lost,' he told her obliquely, pushing back the rebellious lock of hair that Melanie remembered so vividly, so achingly.

'You'll make it up,' she murmured. 'You've been hit in the face before. You'll bounce back.'

'No!' he replied harshly, standing up. 'Not this time.'

Melanie stumbled to her feet, her eyes widening in alarm.

'It's taken me a long time to realise, Melanie, but the money doesn't count, not any more. Hilary was right, forcing me to stay away until I'd come to my senses. She was a wise old woman and I wish I'd known it sooner. My stepfather's cheated me again, but that doesn't matter either. And Amanda—she's never been important. It was almost worth a million to get her out of my hair.'

'You're—you're not going to marry Amanda?' Melanie asked, surprise causing her to blurt out the words.

'Marry Amanda?' he echoed in amazement. His laugh rang out but the mirth was tinged with bitterness. 'Oh, Melanie, you never cease to amaze me. If Amanda were the last woman on this earth I still wouldn't be marrying her, believe me.'

'I see.'

'Do you? I doubt it.' He searched her face again, eyes coming back to focus on hers. 'I doubt it very much,' he murmured, moving to the doorway.

Melanie followed him into the hallway, brushing past in order to open the front door, the current of electricity flaring instantly at the point of contact, flaring, catching, running through her like a flame. Her head shot up, eyes wild, searching his face, recognising at once her flicker of desire mirrored clearly in Chase's tight expression.

He groaned, hands shooting out, catching at her shoulders, pulling her roughly into his embrace, and Melanie melted against him, drawing strength from his arms wrapped around her, holding her close. She raised her face, lips parted, unconsciously offering herself, and he dipped his head, taking possession of her mouth, his lips hard against hers, wounding in intensity, his tongue seeking her tongue, searching out the secret, sensitive parts of her mouth. She moaned softly as his hands roamed the contours of her body, urging her nearer, moulding her to him, desire spreading outwards, consuming every inch of her as Melanie responded to the urgency of his demands, becoming achingly aware of his need of her.

'Melanie, Melanie, Melanie,' he murmured, drawing away for a moment, his lips brushing against her cheek, her throat, her mouth again. 'I love you. I love you, Melanie. I love you so very much,' he crooned, hands stroking the curves of her body, thumbs massaging the outline of her breasts.

'But what about Bermuda?' Melanie protested, her senses reeling, her mind hardly daring to believe what he was saying.

'I don't care. It doesn't matter. It never has,' he insisted thickly, halting her protests with his mouth again. 'You're not the girl Amanda described,' he explained when the kiss came to an end and her cheek was pressed against his shoulder. 'That was a different Melanie, a younger Melanie, not the Melanie I know, not the woman I love. Whatever you were seven years ago, it's not important now. I *know* you. I *love* you. I've loved you since that very first afternoon in your garden when you hooked that lock of hair behind an ear, trailing a smudge of dirt across your cheek. How I stopped myself kissing it away then I'll never know,' he confided, placing a hand underneath her chin, lifting her head, his eyes filled with burning intensity. 'I love you, Melanie,' he repeated, tender fingers stroking the outline of her jaw. 'I love you.'

'And I love you, Chase,' she told him tremulously, his face beginning to swim before her eyes, tears of happiness welling up, spilling over.

'How can you love me after all I've put you through, all the names I've called you, all the unforgivable things I've said?' he asked, wonderment tinged with uncertainty as probing eyes raked her face.

'How can you love me, knowing what you do about me?' she countered gravely, leaving the truth for later. She didn't wait for an answer, lifting her hands, cupping his face, her eyes full of love as she drew his mouth towards her, her kiss tentative at first and then more confident as she felt the tremor run through his body.

He groaned from somewhere deep inside his chest, sweeping her easily into his arms, carrying her across the hall towards the open doorway at the far end.

'This one?' he asked, pausing for a moment on the threshold.

Melanie nodded, smiling shyly into his face, her spirits soaring as he placed her gently on the bed and lay down beside her. He kissed her all over again, filling her with exquisite tenderness as his fingers disposed of the buttons on her blouse, impatiently pushed away the cotton material, snapping open the front fastener of her lacy bra.

He halted then, his eyes on her breasts as one finger traced their outline, his glance rising, locking with hers, a smile of tenderness playing about the corners of his mouth.

'You're so beautiful,' he rasped, bringing his mouth down on hers, competent hands disposing of skirt and skimpy black panties, leaving Melanie naked on the bed, trembling under his appreciative gaze. 'So very beautiful,' he repeated, emotion thickening his voice.

He shrugged himself out of his clothes, moving his body close to hers, side by side, almost touching, frustratingly close till he reached out, gathering her into his arms, the growl of desire deep in his throat filling Melanie

with delight. She pushed forward, increasing the friction
between them, her thrill of pleasure intensifying as she
met with his response, knew that she and she alone had
created that response.

They moved together, Melanie knowing instinctively
how to arouse him, her hands ranging his body, revelling in the strength of him as his mouth moved downwards, circling her breasts, tongue teasing her nipples,
generating waves of emotion while exploring fingers
found other secret parts of her, moist and inviting, lifting
her even higher, driving her to fever pitch.

The hungry mouth moved on, covering every inch,
kissing, gently biting, the pleasure intense as he moved
down her body, top to toe, raining tiny kisses down her
left leg, trailing his tongue erotically up her right, hands
stroking the curve of hip and waist, moving lower,
brushing the insides of her thighs with a feather-light
touch that set her on fire.

Quicksilver ran in her veins and she moaned out loud,
writhing under his touch, the fingers searing, the mouth
branding, Chase's smile broadening as he lifted his head,
locking his eyes with hers.

Melanie smiled tremulously, happiness flooding
through, shining out from smoky eyes, flowing out from
every pore. She ran her hand along his thigh, the taut
body—lean and still lightly tanned—trembling at the
contact, and then Chase moved suddenly, pulling her
into his arms so that Melanie rested against him, above
him, her body fitting the curves of his perfectly, her
blonde hair curtaining her face, brushing his chest. And
over he flipped her, on to her back, his body straddling
hers while Melanie laughed out in delight.

'Happy?' he asked, eyes crinkling as he watched her.

'Very happy,' she told him simply, her message of love transmitted, received, acknowledged, returned, and back again. Her hair spread out across the pillow and he paused for a moment, resting on one elbow, his right hand fanning out the golden locks, framing her face.

'You're so beautiful,' he said again. 'Melanie, I love you.'

The tawny eyes were suddenly serious and Melanie's heart began to beat so loud that she was sure all the world could hear it.

'I love you,' he repeated. 'I love you.' And then his mouth came down, gently parting her lips, taking possession of her mouth while he lowered himself on to her body, his fingers finding her ready, and Melanie moved against him, losing herself in the strength of him. She arched her back at the moment of entry, tensing as his movements faltered, and then instinct came into play as she thrust forward against his hesitation, rekindling the momentum. The awkward moment passed, was lost in a rising tide of passion, their bodies beautifully synchronised as the fireworks exploded inside Melanie's head.

'I don't understand,' he said a long time later, his tender smile filling Melanie with happiness as she lay cocooned in his arms.

'Does it matter?' she asked teasingly, running a finger along the line of his jaw.

He caught her hand, halting it, kissing the palm, triggering another trembling response, the topaz eyes flashing knowingly as Melanie blushed crimson.

'No,' he told her, lazy smile spreading, banishing the worry lines that had etched themselves so recently into the corners of his eyes. 'Just idle curiosity I suppose.

Ah, yes!' he exclaimed. 'I think I'm beginning to understand. Ben is Lauren's child, is that it? It wasn't you
Amanda recognised from Bermuda, but Lauren. Oh, my
love, why didn't you tell me?'

'How could I?' she asked simply. 'You'd met Ben, put
two and two together before I could explain. And it
didn't seem important. It never has to me. He's been
my son since the day he was born and he always will be.
Then later, with all the things Amanda said, well, it was
too late. I'd seen your face, Chase,' she explained gently.
'You were horrified. You wouldn't have listened then,
there was too much stacked against me. And today, when
you brought the subject up, you said it didn't matter.
Thank you.'

'For what?'

'For loving me, despite what you believed, for having
faith in me.'

'That was easy enough,' he told her, kissing away the
pain at the corners of her mouth. 'I loved you and
nothing else mattered. And you don't have to explain
about Lauren either. She was your sister. If you believed
in her then I believe in her too.'

'I'd like to explain,' she told him softly, her happiness
almost complete.

'Later,' he commanded, halting her protest with his
mouth, eager hands beginning to range her body,
drawing fresh responses.

'Later when?' she teased, reacting naturally, her body
lifting up to meet his hands.

'Much later,' he replied huskily. 'When I've kissed you
again, when I've made love to you again, when you've
promised to love, honour and cherish me for the rest of
your life. You *are* going to marry me, aren't you,

Melanie?' he asked, raising his head for a moment, piercing eyes looking into hers, reaching to her soul.

'Later,' she murmured, the laughter gurgling in her throat as she caught his look of wry amusement. 'And that, my love,' she whispered tenderly as the excitement flared between them, 'is definitely a promise.'

Next Month's Romances

Each month you can choose from a world of variety in romance with Mills & Boon. Below are the new titles to look out for next month, why not ask either Mills & Boon Reader Service or your Newsagent to reserve you a copy of the titles you want to buy — just tick the titles you would like to order and either post to Reader Service or take it to any Newsagent and ask them to order your books.

Please save me the following titles:	Please tick	√
DARK RANSOM	Sara Craven	
TAKEN BY STORM	Sandra Field	
LESSON TO LEARN	Penny Jordan	
WALK UPON THE WIND	Patricia Wilson	
WHIRLPOOL	Madeleine Ker	
COERCION TO LOVE	Michelle Reid	
LOVE RULES	Ann Charlton	
HIDDEN MEMORIES	Vanessa Grant	
MAID FOR MARRIAGE	Sue Peters *(Faraway Places)*	
THE SINGING TREE	Anne Weale	
LOVE IS A RISK	Jennifer Taylor	
MIRACLES CAN HAPPEN	Stephanie Howard *(Starsign)*	
BLOSSOMING LOVE	Deborah Davis	
STRONG MAGIC	Christine Greig	
THE STORY PRINCESS	Rebecca Winters	
GOBLIN COURT	Sophie Weston	

If you would like to order these books from Mills & Boon Reader Service please send £1.70 per title to: Mills & Boon Reader Service, P.O. Box 236, Croydon, Surrey, CR9 3RU and quote your Subscriber No:...(If applicable) and complete the name and address details below. Alternatively, these books are available from many local Newsagents including W.H.Smith, J.Menzies, Martins and other paperback stockists from 8th June 1992.

Name:..

Address:...

.....................................Post Code:......................

To Retailer: If you would like to stock M&B books please contact your regular book/magazine wholesaler for details.

You may be mailed with offers from other reputable companies as a result of this application. If you would rather not take advantage of these opportunities please tick box ☐